Voices

VOLUME 2

Contemporary Hymnal

D1132355

WORLD LIBRARY PUBLICATIONS
the music and liturgy division of J. S. Paluch Co., Inc.
3708 River Road, Suite 400
Franklin Park, Illinois 60131–2158

Voices As One®
VOLUME 2

Assembly Edition	WLP 006691
Vocal/Harmony Edition	WLP 006693
Guitar Edition	WLP 006692
Keyboard Edition	WLP 006690
CD Set	WLP 006694

Many of the songs in *Voices As One® Volume 2* are available in recordings, songbooks, and octavos published by World Library Publications. For more information or to order, visit our online store at www.wlpmusic.com.

Project Managers
Ed Bolduc, Norma Garcia, Christine Krzystofczyk, Thomas Strickland

WLP Management Team
Mary Prete, Mary Beth Kunde-Anderson, John Wright, Deb Johnston

Editorial Support
Brian Fife, Deborah Guscott, Mark Hart, Alan J. Hommerding, Keith S. Kalemba, Peter M. Kolar, Marcia T. Lucey, Ron Rendek, Paul A. Tate, Aaron Thompson, Michele L. vonEbers, Jonathan Weber

Production Support
Kathy Ade, Denise C. Durand, Steven R. Fiskum, Rita Larkin, Geovanni Morales, Thomas Schaller, Jeff Turner

Published with ecclesiastical approval
Archdiocese of Chicago
December 16, 2005

WORLD LIBRARY PUBLICATIONS
the music and liturgy division of J. S. Paluch Company, Inc.
3708 River Road, Suite 400, Franklin Park, IL 60131-2158
800 566-6150 • wlpcs@jspaluch.com • www.wlpmusic.com

Preface

Welcome to *Voices As One Volume 2*! In response to the overwhelming success of *Voices As One Volume 1*, we are proud to present this resource that offers twice the amount of new repertoire and contains the "must-have" titles that have become an essential part of contemporary worship throughout the country. *Voices As One Volume 2* brings together the very best contemporary songs of faith from a variety of sources to create one hymnal that provides for the needs of today's music ministers and the communities they serve.

The songs in this volume were selected to be of service at a broad range of occasions when people of faith gather. You will find a wealth of music for the liturgy, including two settings of the Mass. You will also find music for prayer gatherings, penance services, praise and worship, retreats, confirmation, teen nights, concerts, and any other time when you rely on music to open a path to an encounter with our God.

Voices As One Volume 2 contains music you can perform effectively whether your musical resources are very limited or abundant. The repertoire ranges from settings for traditional choirs to praise bands, from rock to choral, rap to lyrical, quiet meditation to corporate expression.

These songs are about life, about the rituals of life, about God among us. The words and melodies collected in these pages reflect life's journey. Many selections are based on scripture, while others are the fruit of prayer, meditation, and worship. All remind us that we are transformed when we allow God to work in us and through us.

We are the voice of the church and together we must proclaim our songs. In our lives and in our prayer may we sing with *Voices As One!*

I raise my eyes to heaven up above, lift up my voice in praise,
rededicate my life unto the Lord; I'll follow in his ways.

REFRAIN

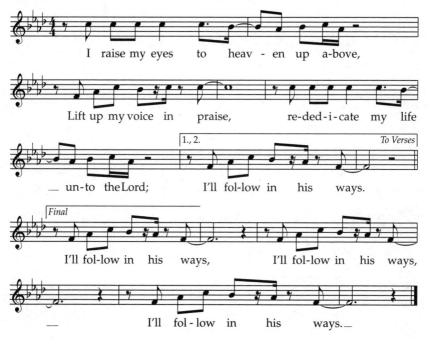

1. Blessed are they who trust him and feel his grace and his power.
   His love will guide and sustain us, yeah, throughout our darkest hour.

2. He gave sight to the blind and set the captive free.
   My life is but pure thanksgiving; he's everything to me.

David Yackley
Text and music © 2003, WLP

201 Above All

VERSE

A-bove all_ pow-ers, a-bove all_ kings, a-bove all_

na - ture and all_ cre-at - ed things. A-bove all

wis-dom and all the ways of man,_____

you were here be-fore the world be-gan._ A-bove all_

king - doms, a-bove all_ thrones, a-bove all_

won - ders the world has ev - er known, a-bove all

wealth and treas-ures of_ the earth,_____

there's no way to meas - ure what you're worth.

REFRAIN

Cru - ci-fied, laid be-hind_ the stone; you

lived to die, re-ject-ed and_ a-lone. Like a rose,

_ tram-pled on_ the ground,_____ you took the fall

and thought of me___ a-bove all.

Lenny Le Blanc and Paul Baloche
Text and music © 1999, Integrity's Hosanna! Music/ASCAP and LenSongs Pub./ASCAP

All the Ends of the Earth/Psalm 98 202

REFRAIN

All the ends of the earth, sing a joy-ful song.___

Sing to the Lord, there is sal-va-tion. All the

ends of the earth, sing a joy-ful song.___ Sing to the Lord,

To Verses | Final

___ there is sal-va - tion.___ Sing to the Lord,

___ there is sal-va - tion.___

1. Sing a new song to the Lord our God.
   For he has worked wonders near and far.
   Our God's right hand and holy arm
   have brought salvation to the world.

2. The Lord has made his salvation known,
   and shown his justice to all lands.
   His truth and love he won't forget
   for all the house of Israel.

3. Let us sing our praises to our God
   with voices blended now in song.
   With harp and horn and trumpet sound
   acclaim the Lord, our God and King.

Bobby Fisher
Text and music © 1994, Bobby Fisher, pub. by OCP

203 All I Need

REFRAIN

You a - lone are all I need, for you hold my des - ti - ny. You a - lone are all I need, O Lord, in you a - lone I am— com - plete.

VERSES

1. So— man - y dis - trac - tions   that pull me a - way.
2. I've set my af - fec - tions   com - plete - ly on you.
3. So I come to your ta - ble   and I hun - ger for you.

1. —   Too man - y at - trac - tions
2. —   There's no more re - jec - tion
3. —   — In your real pres - ence,

1. that lead me a - stray.   But you come to my sens-
2. and no more a - buse.   You— melt my de - fens-
3. my strength is re - newed.   I— taste of your love,

1. - es, Lord,   and you call me your friend,
2. - es, Lord,   and you call me your friend,
3. — my Lord,   in the bread and the wine,

To Refrain

1. and I'm back in your arms— a - gain.___
2. and I'm back in your arms— a - gain.___
3. and I'm back in your arms— a - gain.___

Lincoln Brewster, Danny Chambers, and Israel Houghton
Vs. 3 by Tom Booth
Text and music © 1996, Integrity's Praise! Music/BMI and Praise on the Rock Music/BMI,
admin. by Integrity's Praise! Music

REFRAIN

A-noint - ing, fall on me, a-noint - ing,— fall on me.— Let the pow-er of— the Ho - ly Ghost fall on me. A-noint-ing, fall on me. me.

VERSE

Touch my hands, my mouth and my heart. Fill my life, Lord, ev-'ry part.— Let the pow-er of— the Ho - ly Ghost fall on me.— A - noint - ing, fall— on me.

CODA

me. Let the pow-er of— the Ho - ly Ghost, let the pow-er of— the Ho - ly Ghost, let the pow-er of— the Ho - ly Ghost fall— on me. A - noint-ing, fall— on me. A- noint-ing, fall— on me,———— on me.

Donn Thomas
Text and music © 1992, New Spring (ASCAP), admin. by New Spring

205 Alleluia!

VERSES

1. Joy - ful, joy - ful, we— a - dore you, God of glo -
2. All your works with joy— sur - round you, Earth and heav'n
3. Al - ways giv - ing and— for - giv - ing, Ev - er bless -
4. Mor - tals, join— the might - y cho - rus Which the morn -

1. - ry, Lord— of love; Hearts un - fold like flow'rs
2. — re - flect— your rays, Stars and an - gels sing—
3. - ing, ev - er blest, Well-spring of— the joy—
4. - ing stars— be - gan; God's own love is reign -

1. — be - fore you, O-p'ning to— the sun— a - bove.
2. — a - round you, Cen - ter of— un - bro - ken praise;
3. — of liv - ing, O - cean - depth of hap - py rest!
4. - ing o'er us, Join-ing peo - ple hand in hand.

1. Melt the clouds of sin— and sad - ness;
2. Field and for - est, vale— and moun - tain,
3. Lov - ing Fa - ther, Christ— our broth - er,
4. Ev - er sing - ing, march— we on - ward,

1. Drive the dark of doubt a - way; Giv - er of— im - mor -
2. Flow-'ry mead-ow, flash-ing sea,— Chant-ing bird and flow -
3. Let your light up - on— us shine; Teach us how to love—
4. Vic - tors in— the midst of strife; Joy - ful mu - sic lifts—

1. - tal glad-ness, Fill us with the light of day!
2. - ing foun-tain, Prais-ing you e - ter - nal - ly!—
3. —each oth - er, Lift us to— the joy— di - vine.
4. — us sun - ward In the tri - umph song— of life.

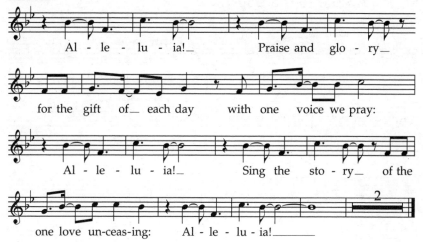

Al - le - lu - ia!_ Praise and glo - ry_
for the gift of_ each day with one voice we pray:
Al - le - lu - ia!_ Sing the sto - ry_ of the
one love un-ceas-ing: Al - le - lu - ia!_____

Text (vss.): Henry van Dyke, 1852–1923
Text (ref.): Paul L. Berrell

Paul L. Berrell
Text (ref.) and music © 2003, WLP

206 Awake to the Day

REFRAIN

A-wake to the day_ of the com-ing of the Lord. Sing
out! Re-joice in this land.___ Make straight the way for the

1., 2.
King-dom of God is at_ hand.___

Final
hand.___ A-wake to the day of the com-ing of the
Lord. Sing out! Re-joice in this land.___ Make straight the way
_ for the King-dom of God is at_ hand.___

1. Signs in the sun and the moon and the stars,
   We prepare for you, Lord.
   Then all shall sing the power of God.
   We prepare for you, Lord.
   As long as the sun shall remain
   so the name of the Lord God will reign.

2. Wrapped in the cloak of justice from God,
   We prepare for you, Lord.
   Gathered at the word of the Holy One,
   We prepare for you, Lord.
   Every mountain and hill be made low
   that the glory of God we may know.

Ed Bolduc and John Barker
Text and music © 2003, WLP

1. As the deer pant-eth for the wa-ter, so my
2. You're my friend and you are my broth-er, e-ven
3. I want you more than gold or sil-ver, on-ly

1. soul long-eth af - ter thee. You a - lone are my
2. though you are a King. I love you more than
3. you__ can sat - is - fy. You a - lone are the

1. heart's de-sire__ and I long to wor - ship thee.
2. an - y oth-er, so much more than an - y - thing.
3. real joy-giv-er and the ap - ple of my eye.

1.–3. You a - lone are my strength, my shield; to you a - lone may my

1.–3. spir - it yield. You a - lone are my

1.–3. heart's de - sire and I long to wor - ship thee.

Martin Nystrom
Text and music © 1984, Maranatha Praise, Inc. (admin. by The Copyright Co.)

208 Be Still and Know That I Am God

REFRAIN/OSTINATO

Be still and know that I am God;

be still and know that I am God.

1. God is a refuge and strength, a helper close at hand,
   close to my distress.

2. So may we not be afraid, though trembling is the earth,
   though all the mountains fall.

3. Though all the waters may rage, the seas press all around,
   my God will be my strength.

4. The rivers resound with great love, the city sings for joy,
   with God we will stand firm.

5. Consider the works of the Lord, the labors God has done;
   all conflict now will cease.

6. The Lord of creation is near, a stronghold deep within,
   "Be still and know God's peace."

Steven C. Warner
Text and music © 1999, WLP

REFRAIN

Be still, my love; know that I am God.

Be still, my love; know that I am God.

1. The mountains shake, the waters roar,
   the valleys tremble with fear,
   and yet our strength, our refuge sure,
   whispers in our ear:

2. Though nations fight, though kingdoms fall,
   though spiteful hearts will harm,
   your mercy holds us, we hear your call,
   we linger in your resting arms as you say:

3. Behold the works out Lord has done
   to change these hearts of stone.
   God breaks our arrows, God breaks our bows,
   God calls us chosen, calls us God's own, saying:

David Kauffman
Text and music © 2002, David Kauffman, admin. by Music Services (BMI)

210 Be Glorified

Your love has cap-tured me. Your grace has set me free.

Your life, the air I breathe. Be glo-ri-fied

1., Final   To Verse   2. To Bridge
Last time

in me.

VERSE

You set my feet to danc-ing. You set my heart on fire. In the

pres-ence of a thou-sand kings you are my one de-sire.

I stand be-fore you now with tremb-ling hands lift-ed high.

3   To Refrain

Be glo-ri-fied!

BRIDGE

Be glo - ri - fied_____ in__ me. Be glo - ri - fied

_____ in__ me. Be glo - ri - fied_____ in__ me.

1. **2.** *To Refrain*

Be glo - ri - fied!__

Louis Giglio and Chris Tomlin
Text and music © 1999, Worshiptogether.com, admin. by EMI Christian Music Pub.

211 Be God's

VERSES

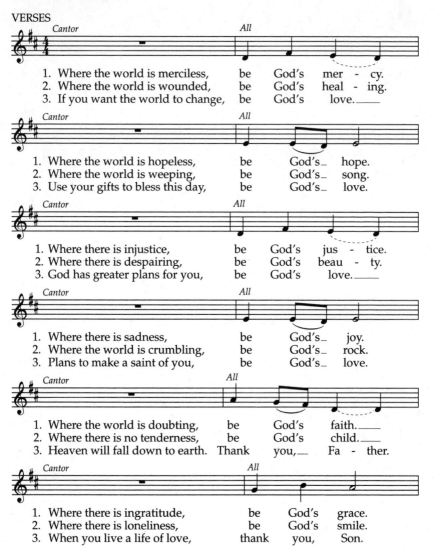

Cantor   *All*

1. Where the world is merciless,   be God's mer - cy.
2. Where the world is wounded,   be God's heal - ing.
3. If you want the world to change,   be God's love.___

Cantor   *All*

1. Where the world is hopeless,   be God's_ hope.
2. Where the world is weeping,   be God's_ song.
3. Use your gifts to bless this day,   be God's_ love.

Cantor   *All*

1. Where there is injustice,   be God's jus - tice.
2. Where there is despairing,   be God's beau - ty.
3. God has greater plans for you,   be God's love.___

Cantor   *All*

1. Where there is sadness,   be God's_ joy.
2. Where the world is crumbling,   be God's_ rock.
3. Plans to make a saint of you,   be God's_ love.

Cantor   *All*

1. Where the world is doubting,   be God's faith.___
2. Where there is no tenderness,   be God's child.___
3. Heaven will fall down to earth.   Thank you,_ Fa - ther.

Cantor   *All*

1. Where there is ingratitude,   be God's grace.
2. Where there is loneliness,   be God's smile.
3. When you live a life of love,   thank you, Son.

1., 2.
Cantor ... All ... Cantor

1. Where there is confusion, be God's truth. Where there is
2. Where the world is dying, be God's life. Where there is

All ... To Refrain 3. Cantor

1. weakness, be— God's strength. 3. The lame will walk, the blind will see.
2. darkness, be— God's light.

All ... To Refrain

3. Thank you, Spir - it. Je - sus dwells in— me!—

REFRAIN

Let your life change the world— one— per-son at— a time.

— Let your life be— the pres - ence of our

Lord Je - sus Christ. As the bread be-comes his— Bod-

- y, we can be the liv - ing sign.— With God's

love, change the world with your life.

Danielle Rose
Text and music © 2003, Danielle Rose Skorich, pub. by WLP

212 Better Is One Day

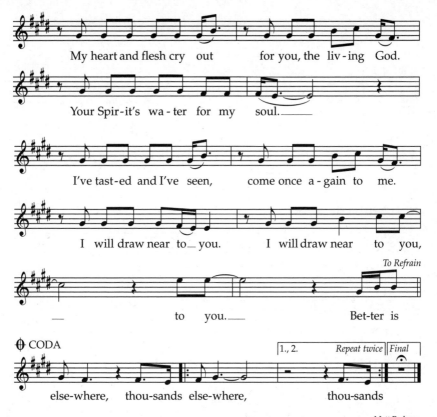

My heart and flesh cry out for you, the liv-ing God.

Your Spir-it's wa-ter for my soul.

I've tast-ed and I've seen, come once a-gain to me.

I will draw near to you. I will draw near to you,

To Refrain

to you. Bet-ter is

CODA

1., 2. *Repeat twice* | *Final*

else-where, thou-sands else-where, thou-sands

Matt Redman
Text and music © 1995, Thankyou Music (KWY)(PRS), admin. by EMI Christian Music Pub.

Blessed Is He (Palm Processional) 213

OSTINATO

Bless-ed is he who comes in the name of the Lord!

Praise to the King of kings!
Praise to Jesus, the King of kings!
Clap your hands, all peoples! Shout to God with joy!
Shout to God, shout to God with joy!
Shout to God, shout to God with joy!
Sing Hosanna! Sing Hosanna!
Praise the Lord! Praise the Lord!

Feargal King
Text and music © 2000, WLP

214 Bless the Lord/Lord, Send Out Your Spirit/ Psalm 104

REFRAIN

Bless the Lord, O my soul, bless the Lord, my soul!

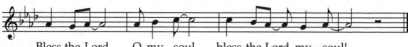

Bless the Lord, O my soul, bless the Lord, my soul!

ALTERNATIVE REFRAIN

Lord, send out your Spir-it. Lord, send out your Spir-it up-on us.

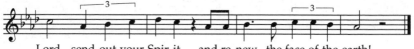

Lord, send out your Spir-it and re-new the face of the earth!

1. Bless the Lord, O my soul,
   O Lord, my God, you are great indeed!
   How many are the works of your hands;
   the earth abounds with your glory.

2. If you remove their spirit, O Lord,
   they wither and return to the dust!
   You send your spirit back and they live,
   you renew the face of the earth!

3. May your glory live forever;
   may your works bring joy to you!
   Let my life be song to your goodness;
   I will rejoice in your name!

Text (refs.) © 1969, 1981, 1997, ICEL

Marcy Weckler Barr
Text (vss.) and music © 2005, WLP

VERSES

1. O bright Moth-er of mer-cy, so pure and so brave,
2. God ex-alt-ed you, daugh-ter, and called you in time
3. Your con-sent to God's Spir-it was fruit-ful and free,
4. Now we hail you, O daugh-ter of mer-cy and light;

1. we hon-or your vir-tue and dig-ni-ty praise.
2. to of-fer your womb to bring forth the di-vine.
3. ac-cept-ing God's Son in a great mys-ter-y.
4. O pray we em-brace peace and good, love and right.

1. Ev-'ry an-gel sa-lutes you, the earth calls you blessed.
2. You were will-ing to serve though you knew not a man.
3. For the Lord you re-mained ev-er-vir-gin in faith,
4. You are splen-did, en-throned a-bove moon, star, and earth.

1. We look to you, Moth-er, for mer-cy and rest.
2. You trust-ed in God and said "yes" to his plan.
3. de-liv-ered from doubt and as-sist-ed by grace.
4. O queen of the heav-ens, your Son saved the world!

REFRAIN

A - ve,____ a - ve,____ a - ve,____ a -

ve,____ a - ve,____ a - ve,____ bless-ed one.

Aaron Thompson
Text and music © 2005, Aaron Thompson, pub. by WLP

216 Blessed Be Your Name

VERSES

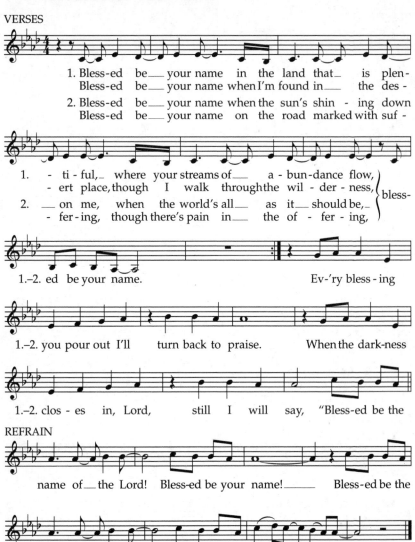

1. Bless-ed be___ your name in the land that___ is plen-
   Bless-ed be___ your name when I'm found in___ the des -
2. Bless-ed be___ your name when the sun's shin - ing down
   Bless-ed be___ your name on the road marked with suf -

1. - ti - ful,___ where your streams of___ a - bun-dance flow,
   - ert place, though I walk through the wil - der - ness,
2. ___ on me, when the world's all___ as it___ should be,___
   - fer - ing, though there's pain in___ the of - fer - ing,

bless-

1.–2. ed be your name.   Ev-'ry bless - ing

1.–2. you pour out I'll   turn back to praise.   When the dark-ness

1.–2. clos - es in, Lord,   still I will say, "Bless-ed be the

REFRAIN

name of___ the Lord! Bless-ed be your name!___ Bless-ed be the

name of___ the Lord! Bless-ed be your glo - ri - ous___ name!"

You give and take a-way! You
give and take a-way! My heart will choose to say, "Lord,
bless-ed be your name!" You name!" "Bless-ed be the

Matt Redman
Text and music © 2002, Thankyou Music (KWY) (PRS), admin. by EMI Christian Music Pub.

Breathe 217

This is the air I breathe, this is the air I breathe,
your holy presence living in me.
This is my daily bread, this is my daily bread,
your very Word spoken to me.

REFRAIN

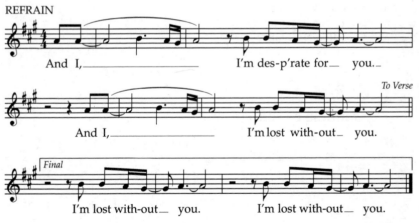

And I, I'm des-p'rate for you.

And I, I'm lost with-out you.

I'm lost with-out you. I'm lost with-out you.

Marie Barnett
Text and music © 1995, Mercy/Vineyard Pub.,
admin. by Music Services o/b/o Vineyard Music Global, Inc. (ASCAP)

218 Canticle of Mary

REFRAIN

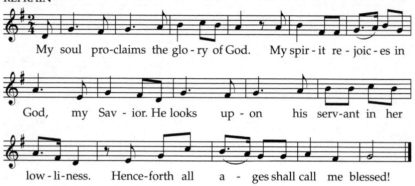

My soul pro-claims the glo-ry of God. My spir-it re-joic-es in God, my Sav-ior. He looks up-on his serv-ant in her low-li-ness. Hence-forth all a - ges shall call me blessed!

1. What marvels my Lord has done for me,
   and holy is his name.
   He showers his mercy on the poor
   from age to endless age.

2. He reveals the strength of his mighty arm
   and scatters the proud and vain.
   He hurls the powerful to their knees
   and sends the rich away.

3. He will raise up the poor and the lowly ones:
   his mercy he remembers,
   the mercy promised from of old
   to the children of Abraham.

Feargal King
Text and music © 2000, WLP

219 Canticle of the Turning

VERSES

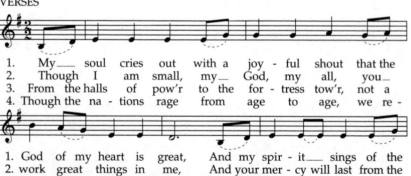

1. My__ soul cries out with a joy - ful shout that the God of my heart is great, And my spir-it__ sings of the
2. Though I am small, my__ God, my all, you__ work great things in me, And your mer-cy will last from the
3. From the halls of pow'r to the for-tress tow'r, not a stone will be left on stone. Let the king be-ware for your
4. Though the na-tions rage from age to age, we re-mem-ber who holds us fast: God's mer-cy__ must de -

1. won - drous things that you bring to the ones who wait. You
2. depths of the past to the end of the age to be. Your
3. jus - tice_ tears ev - 'ry ty - rant_ from his throne. The
4. liv - er_ us from the con - quer-or's crush-ing grasp. This

1. fixed your sight on your serv - ant's plight, and my
2. ver - y name puts the proud to shame, and to
3. hun - gry poor shall_ weep no more, for the
4. sav - ing word that our fore - bears heard is the

1. weak - ness you did not spurn, So from east to west shall my
2. those who would for you yearn, You will show your might, put the
3. food they can nev - er earn; There are ta - bles spread, ev - 'ry
4. prom - ise which holds us bound, 'Til the spear and rod can be

1. name be_ blest. Could the world be a - bout to_ turn?
2. strong to_ flight, for the world is a - bout to_ turn.
3. mouth be_ fed, for the world is a - bout to_ turn.
4. crushed by_ God, who is turn - ing the world a - round.

REFRAIN

My heart shall sing of the day you bring. Let the

fires of your jus - tice burn. Wipe a - way all tears, for the

dawn draws near, and the world is a - bout to_ turn!

Rory Cooney

Traditional Irish melody
Text © 1990, GIA

220 Celebrate the Feast

REFRAIN

We hear the call of our name and gath-er round the ta-ble.__ His pres-ence here in this place is our re-deem-ing grace. He'll lift our hearts, feed our souls, teach us of sweet sal-va-tion,__ re-new our lives, share his peace. Come cel-e-brate the feast.

Last time to Coda ⊕

__ Come cel-e-brate the feast.

VERSES

1. Come, let us sing of our joy__ in the__ Lord;
2. Come, let us bow down and wor - ship the__ King,
3. Come now be - fore him in wor - ship and__ praise,

1. sing out a song__ of sal - va - tion.
2. kneel down be - fore__ him our mak - er for
3. en - ter his gates with thanks - giv - ing for

1. Let us give thanks for his mer - cy and__
2. we are his peo - ple, the flock__ that he__
3. all of cre - a - tion's a sign__ of his__

To Refrain

1. love.___
2. guides.___   Come cel - e - brate the feast.
3. grace.___

CODA

Come cel - e - brate the feast.   Come cel - e - brate the feast.

Come cel - e - brate the feast. __

David Yackley
Text and music © 2005, WLP

221 Christmas Lullaby

1. All is calm in Beth-le-hem, gath-ered 'round the
2. Christ by high - est heav'n a-dored; Christ the ev - er -
3. Now the days are pass-ing on, still we hear that

1. cra - dle, stand. Gen - tle moth - er, bless - ed Child,
2. last - ing Lord. Hail the Child of right-eous-ness,
3. heav'n-ly song; An - gels bend - ing near the earth

1. Sa - cred this night._____ Come all, a -
2. Come and a - dore._____ Look up - on the
3. ech - o their song:_____ Peace on earth, good

1. dore the King! All a - bove re - joice and sing! O,
2. cra - dle stand, Nails shall pierce his feet and hands. O,
3. will to all, born to - day, O Is - ra - el. O,

1. born to reign in ev - 'ry land, this ho - ly Child, these
2. see__ now, our in - fant King shall bear our cross in
3. come, be - hold Em - man - u - el,___ As fore - told,___

1. ti - ny hands. Si - lent night, ho - ly night,
2. suf - fer - ing. Kneel be - fore, kneel and pray,
3. slaves no more. Si - lent night, ho - ly night,

1. sleep, Child, now sleep._____
2. Je - su our Lord._____
3. sleep, Child, now sleep._____

Joe Mattingly
Text and music © 1993, WLP

Christ Has No Body Now But Yours

REFRAIN

Christ has no bod-y now but yours, no hands but yours.— Here on this earth yours is the work, to serve with the joy of com-pas-sion.——

VERSES

1. No hands but yours to heal the wound-ed world,
2. No eyes but yours to see as Christ would see,
3. No feet but yours to jour-ney with the poor,
4. Through ev-'ry gift, give back to those in need:

1. no hands but yours to soothe all its
2. to find the lost, to gaze with com -
3. to walk this world with mer - cy and
4. As Christ has blessed, so now be his

1. suf - f'ring, no touch but yours to bind the bro - ken
2. pas - sion; no eyes but yours to glimpse the ho - ly
3. jus - tice. Yours are the steps to build a last - ing
4. bless - ing, with ev - 'ry gift a ben - e - dic - tion

To Refrain

1. hope of the peo - ple of God._____
2. joy of the cit - y of God._____
3. peace for the chil - dren of God._____
4. be to the peo - ple of God._____

St. Teresa of Ávila, 1515–1582
Adapt. by Steven C. Warner

Steven C. Warner
Text and music © 2003, WLP

223 Come and Gather

REFRAIN

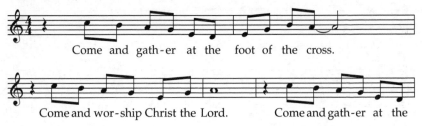

Come and gath-er at the foot of the cross.

Come and wor-ship Christ the Lord. Come and gath-er at the

foot of the cross. O come, let us a - dore.

1. Can you feel the cold, damp air?
   Can you feel the sorrow and despair?
   Come and worship with your tears.
   He'll wash away your fears.

2. Can you see him crucified?
   On the cross our Lord Jesus died.
   Gave his life for you and me,
   he died on Calvary.

BRIDGE
   If we all believe in Christ and accept him in our lives,
   take up your cross and follow him and live again!

John Angotti
Text and music © 2002, WLP

224 Come, All You Blessed Ones

REFRAIN

Come, all you bless-ed ones, blest of a lov-ing God,

en - ter in - to the joy pre-pared for you.

VERSES *Psalm 23*

1. The Lord is my shepherd, I shall not want,
   fresh are the living fields of rest and repose.
   Near gentle waters I am led by the Lord,
   the light of my soul is rekindled.

2. Along holy pathways the Lord takes my hand,
   true to the name of God my journey unfolds!
   If e'er I walk in the valley of death,
   no evil will defeat me.

3. Your crook and your staff are with me this day,
   with rod and a shepherd's staff you give me repose.
   A feast, a banquet the Lord prepares
   in the sight of every people.

4. My head is anointed with precious oil,
   my cup is brimming with your goodness and love,
   they follow me all the days of my life;
   I shall live with the Lord forever.

VERSES *Psalm 34*

1. I will bless the Lord, the Lord, at all times,
   the praise of our living God shall be on my lips.
   My soul shall make its boast in this living God!
   The humble shall hear with rejoicing.

2. Glorify the Lord, our God, with me.
   With one heart and voice let us praise God's name!
   I sought the Lord and my cry was heard,
   from my fears the Lord released me.

3. The angel of the Lord is found in our land,
   around those who honor God to save them from death!
   Taste and see the goodness of our God;
   they are happy who seek the Lord's shelter.

4. The chosen of our God have raised up a cry,
   in all their distress they are rescued from fear.
   The broken-hearted are close to the Lord,
   those whose spirit is crushed God nurtures.

Steven C. Warner
Text and music © 1999, WLP

225 Come and Follow Me

1. We packed our nets to go out to the sea.
   It seemed like any other day.
   And then he came and as I saw him near,
   my soul began to burst like flame.
   He said to me:

REFRAIN

Come and fol - low me.
1. He said to me:
2., 3. He'll say to you:

Come and fol - low me. There you'll find

peace of mind if you just come and fol - low me.

Final

Come and fol - low me. There you'll find

peace of mind if you just come and fol - low me.

2. We are called to cast our nets into the sea,
   traps that will set all people free.
   Our lives are changed, never to be the same.
   Just open up your hearts; he'll call your name.
   He'll say to you:

BRIDGE
This is the time of fulfillment;
just call upon his name and then we'll be saved.

John Angotti
Text and music © 1995, WLP

Come to the Table

REFRAIN

Come to the ta - ble of love.__ Come to the ta - ble of hope._____ Bring all your wor - ries and bring all your fears. Come to the ta - ble of life.

1. Eat the bread of salvation.
   Drink the cup of new life.
   Wine and water, bread and our faith
   become the food for the world.

2. Come and nourish your being.
   Come to refocus your sight.
   Show the earth through your words
   and your deeds: we are the body of Christ.

3. When we come to this table
   we remember, O Lord,
   that you suffered, rose from the dead,
   opened the kingdom again!

FINAL REFRAIN

Come to the ta - ble of love. Come to the ta - ble of hope._____ Bring all your wor-ries, bring all your__ __ fears.__ Come to the ta - ble of life. Come to the ta - ble of life.

John Angotti
Text and music © 2004, WLP

227 Veni, Creator Spiritus

CANON

Ve-ni,—Cre-a-tor Spi-ri-tus. Ve-ni,—Cre-a-tor Spi-ri-tus.

Ve - ni, ve - ni, ve-ni— Cre-a - tor Spi-ri-tus.

John Angotti
Text and music © 2004, WLP

228 Come, Holy Spirit

REFRAIN

Come, Ho - ly Spir - it, send down your fire. Come fill— your

peo - ple, re - new and in - spire. We are— your

chil - dren who long to see— your face, con -

firmed in— one bap-tis - m, one hope, one Lord, one faith.

1. We shall not travel on this road alone.
   We need not fear the darkness,
   for you have sent your fire to light our way
   until we see you again.

2. Called to be merciful for the oppressed,
   called now to be Christ for the poor.
   Send down your Spirit, Lord; make us anew.
   Teach us to be your living sign.

3. Veni, Sancte Spiritus. Send down your fire.
   Veni, Sancte Spiritus. Come, Holy Spirit, come.
   Come, Holy Spirit. Veni, Sancte Spiritus. Send down your fire.
   Veni, Sancte Spiritus. Come, Holy Spirit, come.

John Angotti
Text and music © 2004, WLP

Come, Now Is the Time to Worship

REFRAIN

Come, now is the time to wor - ship.

Come, now is the time to give your heart.

Come, just as you are to wor - ship. Come,

just as you are be - fore your God, come.

VERSE

One day ev - 'ry tongue shall con - fess you are God;

one day ev - 'ry knee will bow.

Still the great-est treas-ure re - mains for those who glad-

To Refrain

- ly choose you now.

Brian Doerkson
Text and music © 1998, Vineyard Songs (UK/EIRE), admin. by Music Services

230 Come, Let Us Sing with Joy

REFRAIN

Come, let us sing with joy to the Lord!

Shout to the rock of our sal - va - tion!

Come, let us greet him with a song of praise, for

great is our God, the King of all kings!

Come, let us sing with joy to the Lord!

VERSES

Cantor

1. Let us bow down and wor - ship the Lord:
2. Great is the Lord and wor - thy of praise:
3. All that has life and breath shall re - joice:
4. Heav - en and earth re - joice in his name:

All

1.–4. Come, let us sing with joy to the Lord!

Cantor

1. For this is our God, whose peo - ple we are:
2. Sing to the Lord and bless his name:
3. The great and the small, all crea - tures of God:
4. He gov - erns the world with jus - tice and truth:

All

1.–4. Come, let us sing with joy to the Lord!

To Refrain

1.–4. Come, let us sing with joy to the Lord!

Come Just As You Are 231

REFRAIN

Come just as you are, hear the Spir-it call.

Come just as you are. Come and see, come re-ceive,

1., 2. *Repeat 1st time* | *Final*

come and live for-ev - er ev-er-more.

VERSE

Life ev-er-last-ing, and strength for to-day.

To Refrain

Taste the Liv-ing Wa-ter and nev-er thirst a-gain.

232 Come Now, Enter/Vengan, Vengan

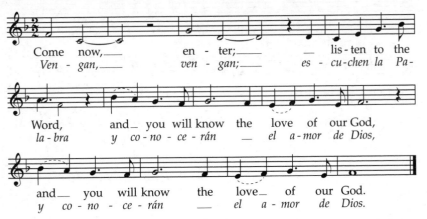

Come now,___ en - ter;___ ___ lis - ten to the
Ven - gan,___ ven - gan;___ es - cu-chen la Pa-

Word, and__ you will know the love of our God,
la - bra y co - no - ce - rán ___ el a - mor de Dios,

and__ you will know the love__ of our God.
y co - no - ce - rán ___ el a - mor de Dios.

Pedro Rubalcava
Text and music © 2002, WLP

233 Come, Emmanuel

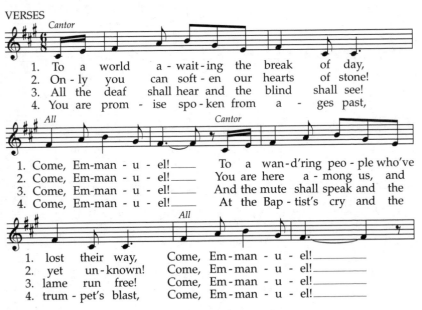

VERSES

Cantor

1. To a world a - wait-ing the break of day,
2. On - ly you can soft - en our hearts of stone!
3. All the deaf shall hear and the blind shall see!
4. You are prom - ise spo - ken from a - ges past,

All   Cantor

1. Come, Em-man - u - el!___ To a wan-d'ring peo - ple who've
2. Come, Em-man - u - el!___ You are here a - mong us, and
3. Come, Em-man - u - el!___ And the mute shall speak and the
4. Come, Em-man - u - el!___ At the Bap - tist's cry and the

All

1. lost their way, Come, Em-man - u - el!___
2. yet un - known! Come, Em-man - u - el!___
3. lame run free! Come, Em-man - u - el!___
4. trum - pet's blast, Come, Em-man - u - el!___

1. Lord of heav-en, yet Vir-gin's child, King by proph-ets fore-
2. In our des-'late and wea-ry land, come and bloom like a
3. Sun of Jus-tice and Prince of Peace, you are light of the
4. When cre-a-tion has passed a-way, robed in glo-ry you

1. told,_____ to shep-herds and wise men, to a
2. rose._____ As light in the dark-ness for the
3. world,_____ who was, and who is, and who
4. come,_____ as rul-er of all things, as the

1. man-ger of hay, Come, Em-man-u-el!_____
2. lost and a-lone, Come, Em-man-u-el!_____
3. ev-er shall be! Come, Em-man-u-el!_____
4. first and the last, Come, Em-man-u-el!_____

REFRAIN

All

Come, Em-man-u-el,_____ and ran-som cap-tive

Is-ra-el!_ Wis-dom a-wake us, rouse us and shake us!

Come, Em-man-u-el!_____

Deanna Light and Paul A. Tate
Text and music © 2001, WLP

234 Come to the Living Stone

REFRAIN

Come to the liv-ing stone, Christ our Lord, who is our strength;
Re - ject - ed— by oth - ers— but cho - sen by God!
— Hal - le - lu - jah!— Hal - le - lu - jah!—

VERSES

1. Built up as liv-ing stones in-to a ho-ly— house,
2. We are a na-tion made to glo-ri-fy the Lord,—
3. Out of the dark-ness God— has called us in-to— light,
4. Once we were not with-in— the mer-cy of our God,—
5. Give praise to God a-bove, and Je-sus Christ the Lord,—

1. — a ho-ly— house, we are a priest-hood cre-
2. — the liv-ing God;— ours is the joy to— re-
3. — a glo-rious light;— once we were lost and a-
4. — the lov-ing God,— now is the gift of a
5. — Re-deem-er Lord,— and to the Spir-it— who

1. a-ted— for praise to— our God a-bove,
2. sound and pro-claim the glo-rious works of— God.
3. lone in— this world, now we be-long to— God!
4. prom-ise— un-furled: God's mer-cy for the— world!
5. dwells in— our hearts, now and for-ev-er— more:

To Refrain

1.-5. — Hal - le - lu - jah!— Hal - le - lu - jah!—

Karen Schneider Kirner and Steven C. Warner

1. Going through the checkout line in the store down the road,
   heard a woman talk about her life and her kids and her heavy load.
   Then it occurred to me that we don't live in a box.
   It's all one world, a gift to us, and this is what I thought:
   We come from different lives, different places, different dreams,
   different faces, different times, but the same God.
   We have different styles, walk different miles,
   different stories, different worries,
   still we are found on common ground.

REFRAIN

We are built on com-mon ground. Love   is   the rock!

2. Taught school to kids I know this morning.
   Each comes from some place I don't know.
   Some are lost, I can see it in their eyes.
   When there's no love around, their parents aren't found,
   we need this common ground.
   We come from different schools, different teachers, different friends,
   all of God's creatures. We are one voice when we praise our God.
   We have different clothes, different homes,
   different churches, but the same hope.
   Still we are bound on common ground.

BRIDGE
   Why do we think we're so different?
   There's more to life than money or material things.
   When you get right down to the bottom of our souls,
   we're connected no matter what we're told,
   so stop fighting over a difference.
   We all walk this common ground.
   Yeah, common ground. *Refrain repeated ad lib.*

3. Different lives, different places, different dreams,
   different faces, different times, but the same God.
   We have different styles, walk different miles,
   different stories, different worries,
   still we are found on common ground.

John Angotti
Text and music © 2002, WLP

236 Create a Clean Heart

REFRAIN

Cre - ate a clean_ heart_ with - in_ me, O
Cre - ate a clean_ heart_ with - in_ me, O

God,_ and I shall be cleansed, I shall be
God,_ and I shall be free, free_ to

made in the like - ness of Je - sus._
love in the like - ness of Je - sus._

VERSES

1. Lord, I have sought for you, God, I'm in need of you,
2. A clean heart brings life to prayer, joy of sal - va - tion bears

1. give me the grace of your love.___ For a
2. fruit for a hun - ger - ing world.___ For a

1. pure heart is gift from you, all things be - com - ing new,
2. life lived in you, Cre - a - tor God, re - news

1. glad - ness and joy re - place fear._
2. all who dare en - ter your heart._

Tom Booth
Text and music © 1995, Tom Booth

Create a Clean Heart in Me/
Be Merciful, O Lord/Psalm 51

REFRAIN

Cre-ate a clean heart in me, O God. Cre-ate a clean heart in me.

ALTERNATIVE REFRAIN

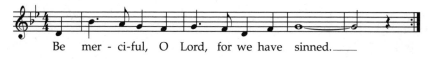

Be mer-ci-ful, O Lord, for we have sinned.____

1. Have mercy on me, O God, in your goodness;
   in your compassion wipe out my offense.
   Thoroughly wash me from all of my guilt;
   and of my sin cleanse me.

2. For I acknowledge my offense,
   and my sin is before me always.
   "Against you only have I sinned,
   and done what is evil in your sight."

3. A clean heart create for me, O God,
   a steadfast spirit renew in me.
   Cast me not out from your presence, O Lord,
   and your holy spirit take not from me.

4. Give me back the joy of your salvation;
   a willing spirit sustain in me.
   I will teach transgressors your ways,
   and sinners shall return to you.

Paul L. Berrell
Music © 2004, WLP

238 Draw Me Close

VERSE

Draw me close to you, nev-er let me go. I lay it all down a-gain to hear you say that I'm your friend. You are my de-sire, no one else will do 'cause noth-ing else could take your place, to feel the warmth of your em-brace. Help me find the way, bring me back to you.

REFRAIN

You're all I want. You're all I've ev - er need-ed. You're all I want. Help me know you are near.

To Verse

Final

Help me know you are near. Help me know you are near.

Kelly Carpenter
Text and music © 1994, Mercy/Vineyard Pub.,
admin. in North America by Music Services o/b/o Vineyard Music Global, Inc. (ASCAP)

REFRAIN

Deep down I know, I must thank God, oh,—
deep down I know, I must thank God!
Deep down I know, I must thank God, oh,—
deep down I know, I must thank God!

1. Lost in the night, I feel the hand of God;
   Deep in my soul, I know God is near!
   When I awake to greet the morning,
   I see the holy light shine before me!

2. My heart is glad, leaping for happiness;
   My God will walk with me, and I'll never die,
   for God will destroy the demons that haunt me;
   forgiving with mercy; giving me peace!

3. Stand up, my friends, and feel the power of God
   stirring within you; answer the call!
   Look all around you, and you'll see the face of God!
   Bound to each other we will be free!

David Haas
Text and music © 1995, GIA

240 Did You Feel the Mountains Tremble?

VERSES

1. Did you feel the moun-tains trem - ble? Did you hear the
2. Did you feel the peo - ple trem - ble? Did you hear the
3. Did you feel the dark - ness trem - ble_ when the saints join

1. o - ceans roar, when the peo - ple rose to sing of_
2. sing - ers roar, when the lost be - gan to sing of_
3. in one song, and all the streams flow as one riv - er_

1. Je - sus Christ, the ris - en One?_____
2. Je - sus Christ, the sav - ing One?_____
3. to wash a - way our bro - ken - ness?_____

To Verse 2 2., 3.

And we can see that, God,

you're mov - ing, a might-y riv - er through the na - tions;

and young and old will turn to Je - sus.__ Fling wide, you

heav-en-ly gates; pre - pare the way of the ris - en

Lord.

REFRAIN

Last time to Final

O - pen up___ the doors. Let the mu - sic play.
Songs that bring your hope, songs that bring your joy,

Let the_ streets_ re-sound with sing-ing:___

danc - ers_ who dance up-on in-jus-tice.

To Verse 3 | Final

danc - ers_ who dance up-on in-jus-tice.

Martin Smith

Text and music © 1994 Curious? Music UK(PRS), admin. by EMI Christian Music Pub.

Dismissal Amen 241

REFRAIN

A-men, a-men, hal - le-lu - jah.

A-men, a-men, hal - le-lu - jah.

A-men, a-men, hal - le-lu - jah.

A-men, a-men, hal - le - lu - jah.

1. Go in the peace of Christ. Go in peace to love and serve.

2. Thanks be to God. Amen. May your work give praise to God.

3. Blessed be God's Holy Name. Glory and praise forevermore.

Denise Pyles

Text and music © 1999, WLP

242 Everything to Me

VERSE 1

1. Ev-'ry mo-ment, ev-'ry nu-ance
since the u-

1. -ni-verse be-gan,— All the beau-

1. -ty that shines through us dem-on-strates

1. your mas-ter plan. Mere words can-not do jus-

1. -tice to— your great-ness,— your right-eous-ness,

1. your glo-rious ways. All peo-

1. -ples will rise up— in ev-'ry na-tion— and cry out

1. your name in—— praise,— in praise.———

REFRAIN

You're the hope I live— for, you're the grace I— need,

— you're the voice that's call-in' out— to me.———

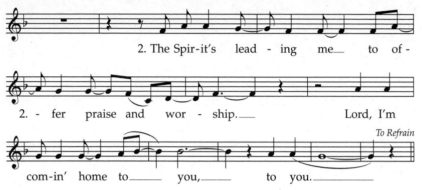

2. The Spir-it's lead - ing me— to of -

2. - fer praise and wor - ship.— Lord, I'm

To Refrain

com-in' home to—— you,—— to you.——

David Yackley
Text and music © 2005, WLP

243 Every Nation on Earth/Psalm 72

REFRAIN

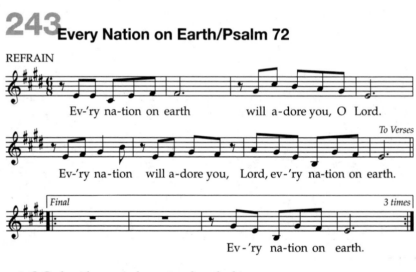

Ev-'ry na-tion on earth will a-dore you, O Lord.

To Verses

Ev-'ry na-tion will a-dore you, Lord, ev-'ry na-tion on earth.

Final   *3 times*

Ev-'ry na-tion on earth.

1. O God, with your judgment endow the king,
   with your justice the king's son.
   Justice shall govern your people in peace
   and fairness your afflicted ones.

2. O justice shall bloom like a flower in his day,
   profound peace till the moon is no more.
   From sea to sea, to the ends of the earth
   may your rule extend.

3. He shall rescue the poor when they cry out to him,
   the afflicted when no one will care.
   Mercy and pity for lowly and small,
   the lives of the poor God will save.

Text (ref.) © 1969, 1981, 1997, ICEL
Text (vss.) © 1970, CCD

Aaron Thompson
Music © 2004, Aaron Thompson, pub. by WLP

REFRAIN

Lord, your love means ev - 'ry - thing, ev-'ry-thing I__ am.__ For your word I'm hun - ger - ing, to un-der-stand your plan. Lord, you taught my heart to__ sing__ be-fore my life be - gan.__ Lord, I'll give you ev - 'ry - thing, ev-'ry-thing I__ am.__

I want to know you.
I want to feel your presence.
I want to love you, Lord, with all my soul.
I want to praise you.
I want to see your glory.
I want to wander down those streets of gold.

David Yackley
Text and music © 2003, WLP

Everything

VERSES

1. With rain, with sun, with much, with less,
2. Your grace, your heart, your voice, your touch,

1. with joy, with pain, with life, with death,
2. your word, your peace, your hope, your love,

1.–2. the on - ly things that sat - is - fy___ come

1.–2. ___ from you, they come from you._____

REFRAIN

Ev - 'ry - thing that's beau - ti - ful,___
 - sand words could not___ ex - plain, a thou-

ev - 'ry - thing that's won - der - ful,___ ev -
 - sand worlds could not___ con - tain___ ev -

1., Final

 - 'ry per - fect gift___ comes from you._____

2., 3. *To Verse 2 / To Bridge*

(⌒) *Last time*

___ A thou- ___ comes from you._____

BRIDGE

Comes from the Fa - ther of Lights,___ ___ comes from the Giv - er of Life,___ comes from the heav- - ens a - bove,___ comes straight from the heart to the peo- - ple you love, from the Fa - - ple you love.___

Chris Tomlin and Jesse Reeves
Text and music © 2002, Worshiptogether.com Songs (ASCAP), and Six Step Music (WTS) (ASCAP),
admin. by EMI Christian Music Pub.

246 Every Move I Make

Ev-'ry move I make I make in you. You make me move, Je-sus.

Ev-'ry breath I take I breathe in you.

Ev-'ry step I take I take in you. You are my way, Je-sus.

Ev-'ry breath I take I breathe in you.

Waves of mer-cy, waves of grace. Ev-'ry-where I look

I see your face. Your love has cap-tured me.

O my God, this love, how can it be? Na na na na na na na,

na na na na na na na. Na na na na na na na, na na na na na na na.

David Ruis
Text and music © 1996, Mercy/Vineyard Pub. and Vineyard Songs (Canada),
admin. in North America by Music Services o/b/o Vineyard Music Global, inc. (ASCAP/SOCAN)

VERSE

Pour your Ho - ly Spir - it up-on me;___

let your pres - ence fill___ me___ up.___

Make my life___ a flow - ing riv - er___

of your ev - er - last - ing___ love.___

REFRAIN

Like a liv-ing stream flow-ing from your might-y o - cean,

pu-ri-fy___ in me my de - sire and my de-vo - tion.

Make my life___ a flow - ing riv - er___

of your ev - er - last - ing love.___

248 Father, We Thank Thee

VERSES 1, 2

1. Fa-ther, we thank thee for plant - ing your
2. vir - gin, Christ lived to

1. seed in our hearts. Fa-ther, we thank thee for Je-sus thy
2. show us your face, full of com-pas - sion for the

1. Son to us im - parts knowl-edge and faith
2. whole hu - man race. Though we are sin - ners

1. and bread for all our days. Thine is the
2. you would not hold back your grace. So through his

1.
1. pow-er, be thine the praise. 2. Born of a

2.
2. dy - ing he lives in ev - 'ry time and place. 3. At the last

VERSES 3–5

3. sup-per, gath - ered with friends so dear,
4. na - tions, e - ter - nal sac - ri - fice,
5. glo - ry! We ac-claim thee through this same Christ your Son.

3. _____ know-ing with - in   that his be-
4. _____ in - no-cent vic - tim,   of - fer - ing
5. __ His bod - y giv - en for our free-dom,   his blood shed that

3. tray - er__ was near,   down on his knees,
4. his own ver - y__ life._ Now the bread we_ eat
5. we are now made one. Through the bread and cup

3. wash-ing their feet,_____   gives an ex -
4. and the cup that we share,_____   his Bod - y and
5. we keep his mem - o - ry._____   Fa - ther, we

3.
3. am - ple. His word is now com - plete.   4. A priest for all

4.
4. Blood, his liv-ing pres - ence__ here.   5. We praise thy

5.
5. thank thee, for Christ has set us free!   Fa - ther, we

5. thank thee, for Christ has set us free!

Bruce Cinquegrani

John Angotti

249 Fountain of Mercy

VERSES

1. Foun - tain of mer - cy,__ mist-ing o - ver me,
2. O - cean of__ di - vin-i - ty,__ mist-ing o - ver me,
3. Riv - er of____ splen-dor, mist-ing o - ver me, I'm

1. per - fect flow of heal - ing, I thirst e - ter - ni-ty.__
2. springs of life__ and bless - ing, I hun-ger pu - ri-ty.__
3. o - ver-whelmed and breath-less; __ whis-per love in my ear.

1. Per - me - ate_ my be - ing, cleanse me from my sin.
2. Sweet mist of mer - cy, car - ried in__ the wind.
3. Your reign is free-dom, wash-ing all_ my fear.

REFRAIN

1., 3. Foun - tain__ of mer - cy, foun - tain__ of mer - cy,
2. Spir - it__ of glo - ry, spir - it__ of glo - ry,

1., 2. To Verse 2 / To Bridge

1., 3. foun - tain__ of mer - cy, mist-ing o - ver me.
2. spir - it__ of glo - ry, mist-ing o - ver me.

Final

me. Foun-tain of mer - cy, foun - tain__ of mer - cy.__

Foun - tain of mer-cy, mist-ing o - ver me.

BRIDGE

Who am I to experience your tranquillity?
No denying your deliverance of our humanity.
Mercy misting all over me, healing sacramentally.
Misting mercy, your mystery holds the truth that sets me free.

Bernie Choiniere and Loretta Choiniere
Text and music © 2002, WLP

REFRAIN

I give my-self a - way   to   hon - or you.

I know this life I live   is   not   my__   own.

Glo - ry   and praise be yours   for - ev - er-more.

I   live   for   you   and you   a - lone.__

1. As the painter brings life to his canvas
   with every brush stroke of his hand,
   so it is with Jesus Christ, who loves us
   as he blesses all the children of the land.

2. Every gift we have comes from our Savior.
   Each of us is blessed more than we can know.
   To the one who gives to us so freely
   let us give ourselves and praise him evermore.

John Towner
Text and music © 1993, WLP

251 Forever Grateful

VERSE

You did not wait for me to draw near to you, but you clothed your-self with frail hu-man-i-ty;— You did not wait for me to cry out to you, but you let me hear your voice call-ing me. And I'm for-ev-er

REFRAIN

grate-ful to you,— I'm for-ev-er grate-ful— for— the cross; I'm for-ev-er grate-ful to you— that you

1., 3. *Repeat Refrain*

came to seek and save the lost.— I'm for-ev-er

2., *Final* *To Verse*

Mark Altrogge
Text and music © 1987, Sovereign Grace Praise/BMI, admin. by Integrity's Praise! Music

1. Forever you call us home.
   Forever you speak the way of love
   as you offer us the grace we need to follow after you,
   as you offer us the grace we need to follow after you.

REFRAIN

Grace fall - ing from on high, well - ing up — from deep — in - side, — hope giv-en to — hum - ble souls, prom - is - es — to lead us home.

2. Forever you say, "Forgive,"
   and that you will drive away the darkness
   and draw us in to celebrate a life that never ends,
   and draw us in to celebrate a life that never ends.

BRIDGE

Oh, if only for the grace to search for what is true.
Oh, if only for the grace to lose ourselves in you.

3. Forever you call my name.
   Forever your heart is open wide,
   begging our weary souls to taste and see the goodness of the Lord,
   begging our weary souls to taste and see the goodness of the Lord.

Michael John Poirier
Text and music © 1992, Michael John Poirier, pub. by Prayersongs Pub.,
exclusive licensing agent, WLP

253 Forever

VERSES

1. Give thanks to the Lord, our God and king.
2. With a might-y hand and an out-stretched arm:
3. From the ris-ing to the set-ting sun.

1.–3. His love en-dures for-ev-er.

1. He is good. He is a-
2. For the life that has
3. By the grace of God we will

1. bove all things,
2. been re-born,
3. car-ry on,

His love en-dures for-ev-er. Sing

1.–3. praise. Sing praise.

2.–3. praise. Sing praise. Sing praise. For-ev-

REFRAIN

- er God is faith-ful; for-ev-er God is strong.

For-ev-er God is with us, for-ev-er.

For-ev- For-ev-er.

Final

For-ev-er. For-ev-

- er._____ For - ev - er._____

Chris Tomlin
Text and music © 2001, Worshiptogether.com Songs (ASCAP),
and Six Steps Music (ASCAP), admin. by EMI Christian Music Pub.

Forever Will I Sing/Psalm 89 254

REFRAIN

For - ev - er will__ I sing_____ the
good-ness of__ the Lord. For - ev - er will I sing
_____ the good-ness of__ the Lord._____

1. God has made a vow to us,
   a promise to us here.
   He forever walks with us
   and makes us strong.

2. Blessed you who know the Lord
   and walk amid his light
   and rejoice to hear his name.
   We are made strong.

3. Blessed you who know the Lord
   and call him by his name,
   for the Lord remembers all
   and keeps his word.

Text (ref.) © 1969, 1981, 1997, ICEL

Ed Bolduc
Text (vss.) and music © 2003, WLP

255 Freedom Reigns

VERSES

1. Where the Spir-it of __ the Lord is, there is free - dom;
2. If you're tired and thirst-y there is free - dom;

1. Where the Spir-it of __ the Lord is, there is free - dom.
2. If you're tired and thirst-y, there is free - dom.

1. Lift your eyes to heav-en, there is free - dom;
2. Give your all __ to Je - sus, there is free - dom;

1. Lift your eyes to heav-en, there is free - dom.
2. Give your all __ to Je - sus, there is free - dom.

REFRAIN

Free - dom reigns in this place, show-ers of mer - cy __ and __ grace, fall-ing on ev-'ry __ face, __ there is free - dom.

Je - sus reigns in this place, show-ers of mer - cy __ and __ grace, fall - ing on ev - 'ry __ face, __ there is free-

1. *To Verse 2* | 2.

- dom. There is free - dom. _____

Michael Larson
Text and music © 1998, Flood Songs (SOCAN)

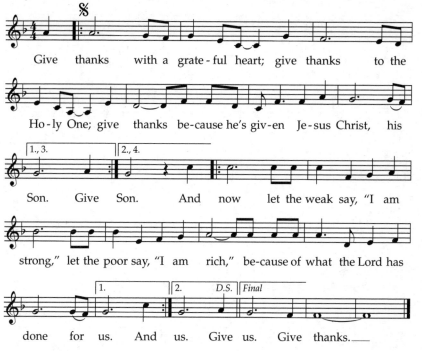

Give thanks with a grate-ful heart; give thanks to the
Ho-ly One; give thanks be-cause he's giv-en Je-sus Christ, his

1., 3. | 2., 4.

Son. Give Son. And now let the weak say, "I am
strong," let the poor say, "I am rich," be-cause of what the Lord has

1. | 2. D.S. | Final

done for us. And us. Give us. Give thanks.___

Henry Smith
Text and music © 1978, Integrity's Hosanna! Music/ASCAP

257 Glorify Thy Name

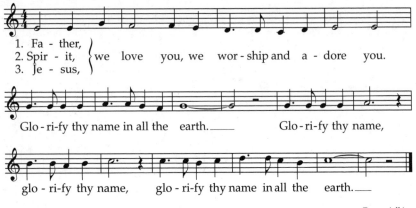

1. Fa - ther,
2. Spir - it,
3. Je - sus,

we love you, we wor - ship and a - dore you.

Glo - ri - fy thy name in all the earth._____ Glo - ri - fy thy name,

glo - ri - fy thy name, glo - ri - fy thy name in all the earth._____

Donna Adkins
Text and music © 1976, CCCM Music, admin. by Maranatha! Music c/o The Copyright Co.,
and Maranatha! Music, admin. by The Copyright Co.

258 Go Make a Difference

REFRAIN

Go make a dif - f'rence. We can make a dif - f'rence.

Go make a dif - f'rence in the world._____

Go make a dif - f'rence. We can make a dif - f'rence.

Repeat first time
Last time to Coda

Go make a dif - f'rence in the world.

VERSES 1, 2

1. We are the salt of the earth, called to let the peo - ple
2. We are the hands of___ Christ reach-ing out to those in

1. see___ the love of God___ in you and me.___ We are the
2. need, the face of God___ for all to see.___ We are the

1. light of the world, not to be hid-den but be seen.
2. spir - it of hope;___ ___ we are the voice of peace.

To Refrain

1.–2. Go make a dif - f'rence in the world.

VERSE 3

3. So let you love shine on,___ let it shine for all___ to

3. see.___ Go make a dif - f'rence in the world.___

3. ___ And the spir - it of Christ will be with us as___ we

To Refrain

3. go.___ Go make a dif - f'rence in the world.

✛ CODA

Go make a dif - f'rence in the world.

Go make a dif - f'rence___ in the world.

Mt 5:13–16

Steve Angrisano and Tom Tomaszek
Text and music © 1997, Steve Angrisano and Thomas N. Tomaszek, pub. by spiritandsong.com®

259 Go Now in Peace

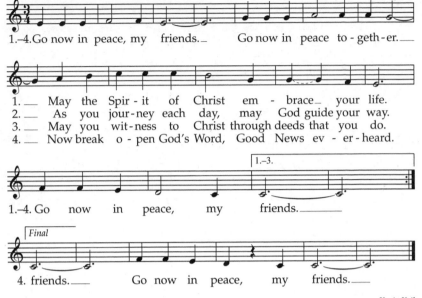

1.–4. Go now in peace, my friends.___ Go now in peace to - geth - er.___

1. ___ May the Spir - it of Christ em - brace___ your life.
2. ___ As you jour - ney each day, may God guide your way.
3. ___ May you wit - ness to Christ through deeds that you do.
4. ___ Now break o - pen God's Word, Good News ev - er - heard.

1.–3.

1.–4. Go now in peace, my friends._____

Final

4. friends.___ Go now in peace, my friends.___

Kevin Keil
Text and music © 2002, WLP

260 Go Now in Peace/Vayan en Paz

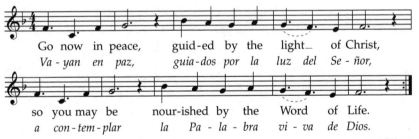

Go now in peace, guid - ed by the light___ of Christ,
Va - yan en paz, guia - dos por la luz del Se - ñor,

so you may be nour - ished by the Word of Life.
a con - tem - plar la Pa - la - bra vi - va de Dios.

Pedro Rubalcava
Text and music © 2002, WLP

REFRAIN

Go out in the world, got-ta go — out in — the world.

Go out in the world, tell ev-'ry-one the Good News! —

Go out in the world, got-ta go — out in — the world,

go out in the world, tell ev-'ry-one the Good, Good News!

VERSES

Cantor

1. Go and make dis-ci - ples — of all — the na - tions.
2. See, the Lord is faith - ful — to all — his peo - ple.

All

1., 2. Go out in the world, tell ev-'ry-one the Good News! —

Cantor

1. Go and make dis-ci - ples — of all — his peo - ple.
2. See, the Lord is faith - ful! — He loves his peo - ple.

All

To Refrain

1., 2. Go out in the world, tell ev-'ry-one the Good, Good News!

Ed Bolduc
Text and music © 2003, WLP

262 God of Wonders

1. Lord of all creation, of water, earth, and sky,
   the heavens are your tabernacle, glory to the Lord on high!

REFRAIN

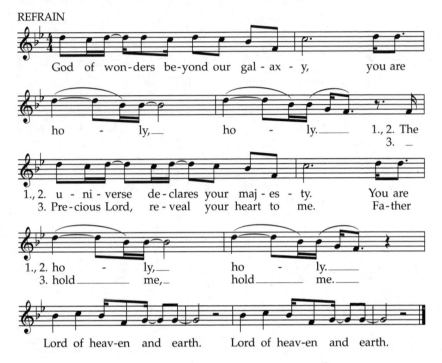

God of won-ders be-yond our gal-ax-y, you are
ho - ly,___ ho - ly.___ 1., 2. The
                                    3. ___

1., 2. u - ni - verse de-clares your maj-es-ty. You are
3. Pre-cious Lord, re-veal your heart to me. Fa-ther

1., 2. ho - ly,___ ho - ly.___
3. hold___ me,_ hold___ me.___

Lord of heav-en and earth. Lord of heav-en and earth.

2. Early in the morning I will celebrate the light.
   When I stumble in the darkness, I will call your name by night.

BRIDGE

Hallelujah to the Lord of heaven and earth.
Hallelujah to the Lord of heaven and earth.
Hallelujah to the Lord of heaven and earth. Holy, holy.

Marc Byrd and Steve Hindalong
Text and music © 2000, Meaux Mercy (BMI), Storm Boy Music, admin. by BMI,
New Spring Pub., admin., by EMI Christian Music Pub., and BMG Songs, Inc.;
and © 2001, New Spring (ASCAP)/Never Say Never Songs (ASCAP)/Meaux Mercy/
Storm Boy Music, admin. by New Spring (ASCAP)

1. You deliver me from evil,
   you show your righteousness.
   You save me from the darkness,
   you bring your truth and light.

REFRAIN

My God is a great God, my God is a great

__ God, my God is a great God, he's a great __

__ God. __ God, he's a great God!

BRIDGE

He's a great, he's a great, he's a great __ God!

He's a great, he's a great, he's a great __ God!

2. In your house are many strangers.
   At your door you heal the sick.
   Blessed are the poor in spirit,
   for they shall be made new.

3. Who is there in all the earth
   in whom I can put my trust?
   Who can move these mighty mountains?
   Whose voice can calm these seas?

David Wilding
Text and music © 1996, Mercy/Vineyard Pub., admin. by Music Services

1. You want to know me? You want to see my face.
   I do not age with time; I do not fit into a space.
   I transcend the capacity of your eye, so who am I?
   It is the question of the moment; it is the question for all time.
   I am you, and you are mine.

REFRAIN

2. I am your father, I am your mother.
   I am the man who cannot cry. I am the story in your eyes.
   I am the orphan of war. I am the leper begging on the corner.
   I am the black slave in chains. I am the Muslim bride who cannot
   show her face.
   I'm the cross you carry again.

BRIDGE

I'm all you have forgotten. I am all that you have not been.
I am in you—all of this is within you. Let the journey begin.
Amen. I am in you. Amen.

FINAL REFRAIN

I_____ am the be - gin-ning in__ the end.   I am the faith

__ in your be - liev - ing.   I am the col - or of   truth.

I am the dream - er   of your   dreams.   I   am   the

fall-ing in__ your love.   I am the words___ of a prayer.

I am the si - lence in the mu - sic.___   I am the mu-

1., 2.   **Final**

- sic.   I__ - sic in the si - lence._____

Danielle Rose
Text and music © 2001, Danielle Rose Skorich, pub. by WLP

REFRAIN

Have_ mer - cy, have mer - cy, Lord. Have mer - cy on us for we have sinned.

1. Have mercy on me, God, in your kindness.
   In your compassion blot out my offense.
   O wash me more and more from my guilt,
   and cleanse me from all my sins.

2. My offenses, truly I know them:
   my sin is ever before me.
   Against you alone, I have sinned:
   what is evil in your sight I have done.

3. Create in me, Lord, a clean heart,
   put a steadfast spirit within me.
   Oh, cast me not away from your presence,
   and take not your spirit from me.

4. Give me again the joy of your help:
   with a spirit of fervor sustain me.
   Open up my lips, O Lord,
   and my mouth shall declare your praise.

REFRAIN

Heal-ing balm we shall be,__ for we are steeped in your mer - cy.__ Send us__ out__ to do your will, O__ God: to be your com-pas-sion and your love.

1. Gentle God, kind and true,
   you are the source of all that is good.
   You sent your Son to be our healing balm;
   in Christ we find forgiveness.

2. Gracious God, we blossom anew;
   fed by the rain of your endless love.
   Steeped in seas of boundless compassion,
   we will go forth to be bearers of hope.

3. Healing God, give us strength
   to be fountains of justice, springs of peace.
   Let us be your outstretched hand
   to a world that thirsts for your mercy. *Refrain twice*

Peter M. Kolar
Text and music © 2004, WLP

267 He Is Risen

REFRAIN

He is ris-en!__ He is ris-en,__ saved us with
un-self-ish love. Lift up your hearts to God a-bove.
Go and tell__ the news you hear to-day.__ He's a-
live_____ and he's with us,__ The ris-ing sun__
in__ the east. Come and share this ho - ly Eas - ter feast.

1. He's alive when we form his body in fellowship,
   when we overcome divisions and build friendships.

2. He's alive when we hear the word, hear the word with faith,
   when we act on that word and live it every day.

3. He's alive when we break the bread,
   he's alive when we share the cup: the food that makes us whole!

John Angotti and Larry Dorsch

John Angotti
Text and music © 2000, WLP

268 Healing Waters

VERSE 1

1. Lord, I've come to touch your face, just to feel__ your warm
1.__ em - brace; come de-scend, Lord, like a dove,
1. touch my heart__ with your love for me,__ for me.__

REFRAIN

Let your heal-ing wa - ters flow_ in this place, let your

heal-ing wa - ters flow_ in this place; you're the giv-er of life,

_ giv - ing new life,_ you're the liv-ing Word of God.

_ Let your heal-ing wa - ters flow_ in this place, let your

heal - ing wa - ters flow_ in this place;

might-y waves of pow'r fol - lowed by your grace, let your

heal - ing wa - ters flow in this place.

VERSE 2

2. Stand - ing in_ this place_ e-ven now_ you're giv-

2. - ing grace; we have seen and we be-lieve, it's by faith

To Refrain

2. _ that we_ re - ceive, we re - ceive._

Chris Springer and Eric Nuzum Thomason
Text and music © 1999, Integrity's Hosanna! Music/ASCAP and Integrity's Praise! Music/BMI

269 Here I Am

1. When I looked into the mirror
   and finally realized all my fears
   were taking over my life,
   I knew it was time to reflect real hard about
   all that I had done that was wrong.
   It was time to make a change.
   So I thought real hard about the difference it'd make
   if I'd lose the fears of making a mistake
   and use the gifts God gave me to use.
   So I opened up my Bible (a good place to start)
   to find what was common in a faithful heart,
   and I found Abraham said these words
   when his arms were weighing heavy.
   Moses said it, too, on the mountain.
   Samuel spoke this invocation when he was just a boy.
   Mary said, "Yes, my Lord," responded with three little words:

REFRAIN

Here I__ am,__ here I__ am,_____ here I__ am__ of my own free will. Send me, Lord,_____ to do your will._____

2. Now that I'm aware of things
   and know that there is more to me
   than just another face,
   I need to take my life in my hands
   and do the work that God commands,
   even if I don't know my fate.
   I've got to trust in what I cannot see
   and know that Christ delivered me
   from my fears of darkness.

So I opened up my Bible (a good place to start)
to find what was common in a faithful heart,
and I found Jesus in the garden down upon his knees,
nailed to the cross on Calvary.
I found Jesus resurrected from the grave.
Jesus said, "Yes, my Lord." I must say "Yes" to my Lord.

CODA

4 times

Here I am.   Here I am. Here I am.   Here I am to do— your will.

John Angotti
Text and music © 2004, WLP

Here I Am to Worship 270

1. Light of the world, you stepped down into darkness, opened my eyes,
   let me see beauty that made this heart adore you,
   hope of a life spent with you.

REFRAIN

So here I am to wor-ship, here I am to bow down, here I am to

say that you're my   God.   And you're al-to-geth-er love - ly,

al-to-geth-er wor-thy, al-to-geth-er won-der-ful to   me.—

2. King of all Kings, O so highly exalted, glorious in heaven above,
   humbly you came to the earth you created,
   all for love's sake became poor.

BRIDGE
   And I'll never know how much it cost to see my sin upon that cross.
   And I'll never know how much it cost to see my sin upon that cross.

Tim Hughes
Text and music © 2001, Thankyou Music (KWY) (PRS), admin. by EMI Christian Music Pub.

271 Here I Am

REFRAIN

Here I am, stand-ing right be-side you.
Here I am; do not be a-fraid. Here I am,
wait-ing like a lov-er. I am here; here I am.

1.–3. To Verses

Final

am. I am here; here I am.

1. Do not fear when the tempter calls you.
   Do not fear even though you fall.
   Do not fear, I have conquered evil.
   Do not fear; never be afraid.

2. I am here in the face of every child.
   I am here in every warm embrace.
   I am here with tenderness and mercy.
   Here I am; I am here.

3. I am here in the midst of every trial.
   I am here in the face of despair.
   I am here when pardoning your brother.
   Here I am; I am here.

Tom Booth
Text and music © 1996, Cristo Music, pub. by spiritandsong.com®

High and Exalted 272

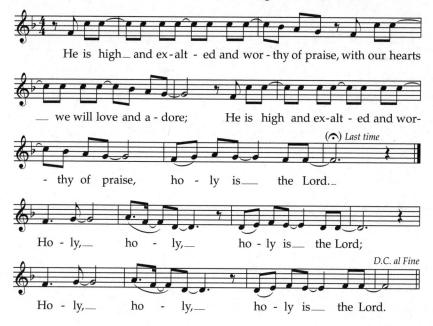

He is high and ex-alt-ed and wor-thy of praise, with our hearts

— we will love and a-dore; He is high and ex-alt-ed and wor-

(⌢) *Last time*

-thy of praise, ho-ly is the Lord.

Ho-ly, ho-ly, ho-ly is the Lord;

D.C. al Fine

Ho-ly, ho-ly, ho-ly is the Lord.

Kyle Rasmussen
Text and music © 1996, Integrity's Hosanna! Music/ASCAP

Holy Ground 273

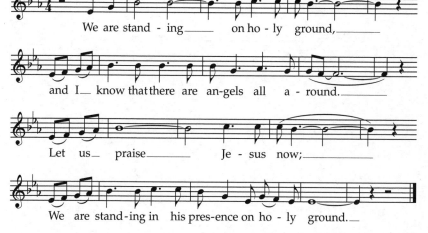

We are stand-ing on ho-ly ground,

and I know that there are an-gels all a-round.

Let us praise Je-sus now;

We are stand-ing in his pres-ence on ho-ly ground.

Geron Davis
Text and music © 1983, Meadowgreen Music (ASCAP)/ Songchannel Music Co. (MG) (ASCAP)

274 Hope to Carry On

VERSES

1. I can see Je - sus   hang-in' on the cross.
2. I can hear Je - sus   say-ing "Fa-ther for-give."
3. You know Pe - ter   put a - way his sword.

1. I can see Je - sus   hang-in' on the cross.
2. I can hear Je - sus   say-ing, "Fa-ther for-give."___
3. I can see Pe - ter   put-ting a - way_ his sword._____

1. I can see Je - sus   hang-in' on the
2. I can hear Je - sus   say-ing, "Fa - ther for - give."
3. I can see Pe - ter,   he put a - way his

1. cross.   He came look-ing for the lost._
2. ___   What a thing_ he___ did._
3. sword.   He won't fight_ no___ more.

REFRAIN

Love has come,   love has come,   love has come, and it's

To Verses

giv-en me hope to car - ry on.___

Final

Love has come,   love has come,   love has come,

and it's giv-en me hope to car - ry on. __

BRIDGE *following Verse 2*

I can see love; love is all I want to see.
Love can make a beggar rich and set a prisoner free.
I know he can do it for you; God knows he did it for me.
I can see love; love is all I want to show you.
Love, love is all a man might need to know; this I know.

Rich Mullins
Text and music © 1990, BMG Songs (ASCAP)

Holiness Is Faithfulness **275**

REFRAIN

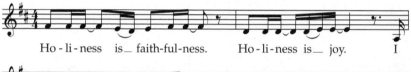

Ho - li - ness is __ faith-ful-ness. Ho - li - ness is __ joy. I

am not bound to lone - li - ness when I fol-low Christ, my Lord.

1. I am looking for my Lord.
   I am looking for my way.
   Must I sacrifice my glory?
   Will I die in living shame?

   Take your cross and follow me.
   Follow my steps and you will see.
   Give it up and you'll be free.
   Do not fear death; you'll rise in me.

2. I have lost my strength; I've fallen.
   My mother, Mary, whispers,
   I am so afraid.
   Will you bear with me my burden?

   Rise up, Son, to your feet.
   In my heart you'll always be with me.
   Here comes Simon of Cyrene.
   Jesus, behind you I will carry.

3. She gazes in my eyes.
   I have fallen once again,
   Daughters of Jerusalem,
   Father, catch me in your arms,

   Veronica kneels at his feet.
   And she wipes the face that bleeds.
   Do not weep for me!
   For I am strong when I am weak.

4. You know that I love you.
   I lay down my life for my friends.
   They have pierced my hands and feet.
   On a tree between two thieves.

   No greater love than this.
   Jesus' body now is stripped.
   Crucified the heavenly king
   Jesus redeemed the world from sin.

Danielle Rose
Text and music © 2003, Danielle Rose Skorich, pub. by WLP

276 Holy Is Your Name

VERSES

1. My___ soul is filled with joy___ as I
2. I am low - ly as a child, but I
3. I pro - claim the pow'r of God, you do
4. To the hun - gry you give food, send the
5. In your love you now ful - fill___ what you

1. sing to God my sav - ior: you have looked up - on your
2. know from this day for - ward that my name will be re -
3. mar - vels for your serv - ants; though you scat - ter the proud -
4. rich a - way___ emp - ty. In your mer - cy you are
5. prom - ised to your peo - ple. I will praise you, Lord, my

1. serv - ant, you have vis - it - ed your peo - ple.
2. mem - bered, for___ all will call me bless - ed.
3. heart - ed and de - stroy the might of princ - es.
4. mind - ful of the peo - ple you have cho - sen.
5. sav - ior, ev - er - last - ing is your mer - cy.

REFRAIN

And___ ho - ly is your name through all gen - er - a - tions!

Ev - er - last - ing is your mer - cy to the peo - ple you have

cho - sen, and___ ho - ly is your name.

David Haas
Text © 1995, GIA

Irish traditional melody

REFRAIN

1. When the Lord brought back Zion from bondage,
   we awoke from our exile's long dream;
   then our mouths were filled with our laughter,
   our spirits with song.

2. The heathens themselves say,"What glories!
   Such great things their Lord works for them!"
   What marvels the Lord worked for us;
   indeed we were glad!

3. Restore us our fortunes, O Lord!
   Rain down, fill these streams in dry land!
   Those who are sowing in tears
   will sing when they reap!

Ken Macek
Text and music © 2000, WLP

278 How Beautiful

VERSES 1, 2

1. How beau - ti - ful___ the hands__ that served__ the
2. How beau - ti - ful___ the heart__ that bled,__ that

1. wine and the bread and the sons of the earth. How__
2. took all my__ sin and__ bore it in - stead. How__

1. __ beau - ti - ful the feet__ that walked the long dust - y__
2. __ beau - ti - ful the ten - der eyes that choose to for -

1. roads and the hill__ to the cross. How___ beau - ti -
2. give and__ nev - er__ de - spise. How___ beau - ti -

1.–2. ful,___ how__ beau - ti - ful,___ how

1.–2. __ beau - ti - ful___ is the Bod - y__ of

1.
Christ.___

2.
Christ.

BRIDGE

And as he laid down his life, we of-fer_ this sac-ri-fice_ that we will live just as he_ died: will-ing to____ pay the price, will-ing to_ pay____ the price.____

VERSE 3

3. How beau-ti-ful_ the ra-diant bride who waits for her groom with his light in her eyes. How_ beau-ti-ful when hum-ble_ hearts give the fruit of pure lives so that oth-ers_ may live. How_ beau-ti-ful,____ how_ beau-ti-ful,____ how_ beau-ti-ful____ _ is the Bod-y of Christ.____ 4. How

VERSE 4

4. beau - ti - ful __ the feet that bring the sound of good

4. news and the love of __ the King. How __ beau - ti -

4. ful the hands that serve the wine and the bread

4. and the sons of the earth. How __ beau - ti - ful, __

4. __ how __ beau - ti - ful, __ how __

4. __ beau - ti - ful __ is the Bod-y of Christ. __

Twila Paris
Text and music © 1990, Ariose Music and Mountain Spring Music,
admin. by EMI Christian Music Pub.

I Abandon Myself

REFRAIN

I a-ban-don my-self to your will.

Do with me what-ev - er you want.

I will on-ly be grate-ful for what-ev-er you do.
With-out an-y con-di - tions and with con - fi - dence

2nd time to Coda

I'm pre-pared for an - y-thing at all.
be - cause you are my God.

VERSE

I com-mit my life to your hands. I

of-fer it all up to you. With all the af - fec - tion of my

To Refrain

heart and my soul be - cause, O Lord, I love you.

CODA

I a-ban-don my-self to your will. I a-ban-don my-self

to your will. I a-ban-don my-self to your will.

John Michael Talbot
Text and music © 2000, Troubador for the Lord Music (ASCAP), admin. by Music Services

I Am the Bread of Life

REFRAIN

I am the Bread of Life bro-ken for the world, I am the
cup poured out for all.___ Those who be-lieve in me will
nev - er die.___ I am the life of the world.

VERSES

1. I am the food that the world can - not give.
2. I am the Word___ from the be - gin - ning with God.
3. I am the truth,___ the new law giv - en in love.
4. I am the sick,___ the fright-ened, and con - fused.
5. I am your friend;___ I'll al - ways walk_ with you._

1. The food and drink___ for those who hun-ger and thirst.
2. I am the Word___ a - live and with_ you now.__
3. I am the way;___ my words are spir - it and life.__
4. I am the lost,___ _ need-ing shel-ter and food._
5. Don't be a - fraid,___ I gave my life for__ you.__

1. I am the true bread sent from heav - en.
2. I am the Word-made-Flesh a - mong__ you.
3. _ I am mer - cy and for - give - ness. }You will
4. I speak the word with pow'r to heal the world.
5. _ I will walk with you for - ev - er.)

To Refrain

1.–5. have e - ter - nal life.___

Tom Kaczmarek
Text and music © 2005, WLP

1. How can this be? Of all the things I know are true,
   I saw them drive the nails into you
   upon the cross. I felt so lost.
   Every dream that ever mattered
   was hung upon that tree and shattered;
   just what I feared.

2. And now I hear they say that you've been raised in glory,
   but how can I believe this story until I see?
   Then you came to me.
   I swallowed all my earthly pride
   and put my hands into your side
   to end all doubt. I'll shout it out:

REFRAIN

I do believe! In your ris-ing from the dead, I do be-lieve___ that you did just what you said: through the pow-er of___your love, tri-umphed o-ver death's de-ceit. ___ O___ my Lord and my God, I do be-lieve!

3. And now I see. Blest are those who have not seen you
   but never doubt how much they need to
   know your grace. I'll sing your praise.
   Because you live, no more to die,
   all God's creation's glorified.
   You set us free eternally.

David Yackley
Text and music © 2003, WLP

I Can Only Imagine

1. I can only imagine what life will be like
   when I walk by your side.
   I can only imagine what my eyes will see
   when your face is before me.
   I can only imagine.

REFRAIN

Sur-round-ed by your glo-ry, what will my heart feel?__ Will I dance

for you, Je - sus, or in awe of you be still? Will I stand

in__ your pres-ence or to my knees will I fall?__ Will I sing,

"Hal - le - lu - jah"? Will I be a-ble to speak at all? I can on-ly__

1.
__ i - mag - ine. I can on-ly i - mag - ine.__

2.
I can on-ly i - mag - ine.__

2. I can only imagine when that day comes
   and I find myself standing in the Son.
   I can only imagine when all I will do
   is forever, forever worship you.
   I can only imagine.

CODA
   Surrounded by your glory, what will my heart feel?
   Will I dance for you, Jesus, or in awe of you be still?
   Will I stand in your presence or to my knees will I fall?
   Will I sing "Hallelujah"? Will I be able to speak at all?
   I can only imagine. Yeah. I can only imagine.
   I can only imagine, yeah, I can only imagine.
   I can only imagine. I can only imagine.
   I can only imagine when all I will do
   is forever, forever worship you.
   I can only imagine.

Bart Millard
I Can Only Imagine is a trademark of Simpleville Music, Inc. Used by permission.

283 I Could Sing of Your Love Forever

VERSE

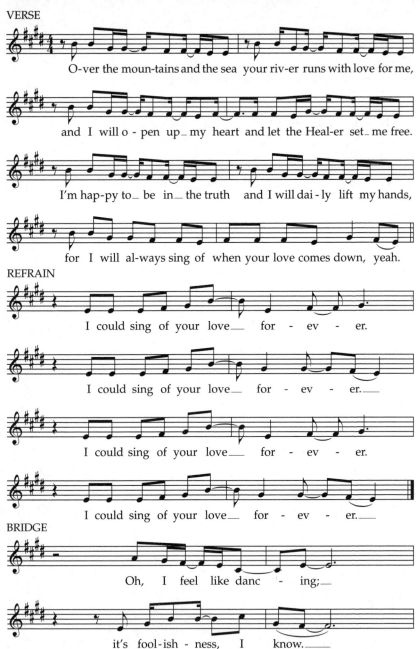

O-ver the moun-tains and the sea your riv-er runs with love for me,

and I will o - pen up my heart and let the Heal-er set me free.

I'm hap-py to be in the truth and I will dai - ly lift my hands,

for I will al-ways sing of when your love comes down, yeah.

REFRAIN

I could sing of your love for - ev - er.

I could sing of your love for - ev - er.

I could sing of your love for - ev - er.

I could sing of your love for - ev - er.

BRIDGE

Oh, I feel like danc - ing;

it's fool-ish - ness, I know.

But when the world has seen ___ the light, they will dance

To Refrain

___ with joy ___ like we're danc - ing now. ___

Martin Smith
Text and music © 1994, Curious? Music UK (PRS), admin. by EMI Christian Music Pub.

I Know That My Redeemer Lives 284

REFRAIN

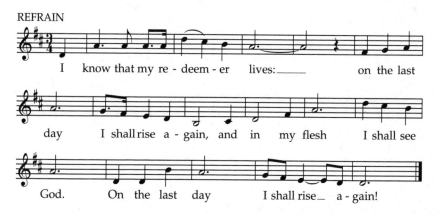

I know that my re - deem - er lives: ___ on the last

day I shall rise a - gain, and in my flesh I shall see

God. On the last day I shall rise ___ a - gain!

1. I shall see my Savior's face,
   and my own eyes shall behold my God.
   On the last day I shall rise again!

2. Within my heart this hope I hold,
   that in my flesh I shall see my God.
   On the last day I shall rise again!

David Haas
Text and music © 1990, GIA

285 I Rejoiced/Psalm 122

REFRAIN

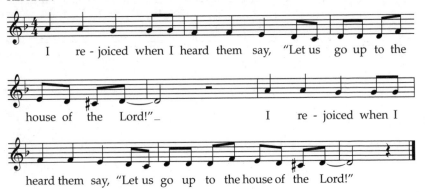

I re-joiced when I heard them say, "Let us go up to the house of the Lord!"_ I re-joiced when I heard them say, "Let us go up to the house of the Lord!"

1. I was glad when they said to me, "Let us go to the house of God!"
   And now our feet are standing within your gates, O Jerusalem!

2. Jerusalem is a city built on unity and strength.
   There the tribes of the Lord sing songs of praise to the God of Israel!

3. Peace to you, peace to Jerusalem!
   May all within your walls dwell in peace!
   For the sake of all my friends I will say, "Peace, Jerusalem!"
   For the sake of the house of God I will speak of your might!
   And I will sanctify your name! I will sanctify your name!
   I will sanctify your name, O Lord!

Feargal King
Text and music © 2000, WLP

286 I Received the Living God

REFRAIN

I re-ceived the liv-ing God,_ and my heart is full of joy.__ I re-ceived the liv-ing God, and my heart__ is full of joy.

VERSES

1. Je - sus said: I   am   the   Bread
2. Je - sus said: I   am   the   Vine,
3. Je - sus said: I   am   the   Way;
4. Je - sus said: I   am   the   Truth;
5. Je - sus said: I   am   the   Life
6. Je - sus said: I   am   the   light
7. Je - sus said: I   am   the   gate,
8. Taste and see,   come bless   the   Lord;
9. In my grief,   I   called   the   Lord;

1. Knead-ed long to give you   life;____   You who will
2. And my branch-es you shall   be;____   Come and drink
3. And my Fa - ther longs for   you;____   So I come
4. If you fol - low close to   me,____   You will know
5. Far from whom noth-ing can   grow,__   But re - ceive
6. Shin - ing for e - ter - ni - ty;____   Go and be
7. Gen - tle shep-herd of my   sheep;_   I will give
8. Let your voice be filled with   praise;_   Glo - ri - fy
9. In his love he an-swered   me;____   You will know

To Refrain

1. par-take of me   Need not ev - er fear to   die.__
2. the sav - ing cup,   Till the King-dom you shall   see.__
3. to bring you home   To be one with us a -   new.__
4. me in your heart,   and my word shall make you   free.__
5. this bread and cup,   And my Spir - it you shall   know.
6. the light of life   Shin - ing for the world to   see.__
7. my life for them,   Show them love that runs so   deep.
8. the Lord with me,   Give him glo - ry all your   days.
9. the love of Christ   if you will but taste and   see.__

Bernard Geoffrey
Vs. 2: Alan J. Hommerding
Vss. 6–9: Brett Ballard

Brett Ballard
Text (vss. 2, 6–9) and music © 1994, 2005, WLP

287 I Send You Out

1. I baptize you in the name of the Father.
   I baptize you in the name of the Son.
   I baptize you with the Holy Spirit.
   Go out and spread Good News!

REFRAIN

I send you out___ on a mis-sion of love. I send you out ___ on a mis-sion of love. I send you out___ on a mis-sion of love, and know that I___ am with ___ you al - ways un - til the end of the world.

2. Well, it's time for us to become people with spirit.
   It's time for us to become people of love.
   It's time for us to know that Jesus Christ is risen,
   forgives our sins, and brings new life!

John Angotti
Text and music © 2000, WLP

288 I Say "Yes," Lord/Digo "Sí," Señor

VERSES

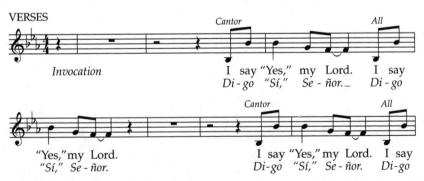

Cantor   All

Invocation   I say "Yes," my Lord.   I say
              Di - go "Sí," Se - ñor.___ Di - go

          Cantor   All

"Yes," my Lord.   I say "Yes," my Lord.   I say
"Sí," Se - ñor.   Di - go "Sí," Se - ñor.   Di - go

1. To the God who cannot die: I say "Yes,"… *Digo "Sí,"…*
   To the One who hears me cry:
   To the God of the oppressed:
   To the God of all justice:

2. I am a servant of the Lord: I say "Yes,"… *Digo "Sí,"…*
   I'm a worker in the fields:
   I'm a prisoner of their wars:
   Like a politician, inevitably:

3. For the dream I have today: I say "Yes,"… *Digo "Sí,"…*
   To be a healer of all pain:
   To come to love my enemies:
   For your peace in all the world:

4. Like that of Job, unceasingly: I say "Yes,"… *Digo "Sí,"…*
   Like that of Maria wholeheartedly:
   Like that of David in a song:
   Like Israel, for you I long:

Donna Peña
Text and music © 1989, GIA

VERSES

1. Lord, you're lead - ing me with a cloud by day
2. And you take__ my hand and you wash it clean.
3. And the ea - gle flies and the riv - ers run.
4. Well, the grass__ will die and the flow - ers fall,

1. and then__ in__ the night the glow of a burn-ing flame.
2. I know the prom - ised land is light years a - head of me.
3. I look__ through the night, and I can see the ris - ing sun.
4. but your__ word's a - live and will be__ af - ter all.

REFRAIN

And ev -'ry-where I go__ I see you. Ev'ry-

where I go__ I see you. **1.** *To Verse 2* **2.–4.** And ev -'ry-

where I go__ I see you **1., 2.** *To Verse 3, 4* Ev'ry-where I go__ I see you.

Final

And ev-'ry-where I go__ I see you Ev'ry-

where I go__ I see you. And ev-'ry-where I go__ I see you.

Ev -'ry - where I go__ I see you.

Rich Mullins
Text and music © 1991, BMG Songs, Inc. (ASCAP)

1. When I'm tired and weak, my life's gone down the wrong track,
   I dig into my soul and I try to remember back.
   When I was a child my life was worry-free.
   I trusted in your love, knew that you would rescue me,
   for I learned you're present here with me in sacraments and signs.
   The mystery of my faith, blind love that gives me strength,
   based upon the fact you loved me.

REFRAIN

And I sur-vive be-cause you love me._ And I sur-vive. I looked death right in_ the_ face. And I sur-vive the strug-gle be-cause you love me, my Sav-ior, my con-fi-dant, the be-gin-ning and the end, my for-giv-er,_ my friend.

Final

giv-er,_ my friend._

2. Try to live my life straight as can be.
   Satan just keeps on coming. Well, he tempts me.
   He knows my weakness, placed it out in front of me to see.
   Well, I slipped and fell into his trap, thought I would never be free.
   But I know you're present here with me in sacraments and signs.
   The mystery of my faith, blind love that gives me strength,
   based upon the fact you loved me.

BRIDGE

I find joy in the sadness. I find hope through the madness.
When the storms of life blow in, I know that I can win.
My faith has set me free, a wonderful mystery
based upon the fact you love me.

John Angotti
Text and music © 2002, WLP

291 If Today You Hear His Voice/Psalm 95

REFRAIN

If to - day_____ you hear_____ his voice,_____

_____ hard - en not_____ your hearts._____

1. Come, let us sing to the Lord, the rock of our salvation.
   Enter his presence with thanksgiving, singing joyful songs.

2. Come, let us bow down in worship before the Lord.
   We are the sheep he shepherds, we are the flock he guides.

Text (ref.) © 1969, 1981, 1997, ICEL

W. Clifford Petty
Text (vss.) and music © 2004, WLP

1. Here I am, humbly before you
   finding my part in your plan;
   for you're my light, my guiding shepherd.
   Lord, can you help me understand?

2. At times I find myself discouraged,
   the journey seems to be so long, yeah,
   but every step I know you're with me.
   You give me strength to carry on, strength to carry on.

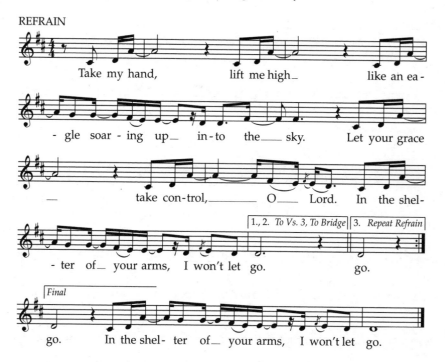

REFRAIN

Take my hand, lift me high like an ea-gle soar-ing up in-to the sky. Let your grace take con-trol, O Lord. In the shel-ter of your arms, I won't let go.

1., 2. To Vs. 3, To Bridge | *3. Repeat Refrain*

go.

Final

go. In the shel-ter of your arms, I won't let go.

3. The wind is howling all around me,
   but you are refuge, safe and warm,
   and through your quiet voice of mercy
   you are calm amidst the storm, calm amidst the storm.

BRIDGE
   I know the road you choose may not be easy, Father,
   but I'm prepared to go where you lead me.
   My home is ready now, a place that's like no other,
   where I will live my days, and I will sing your praise forever, forever.

David Yackley
Text and music © 2003, WLP

293 In Every Age

REFRAIN

All ... *Cantor*

In ev-'ry age, you have been our ref-uge.

All ... *Cantor*

In ev-'ry age, Lord, you have been our strength.

All ... *Cantor*

In ev-'ry way, your peo-ple will a-dore you and we'll

All

lift your name on high. Ho-ly, ho-ly Lord!

VERSES

All ... *Cantor*

1. In the days of old when Mo-ses led the peo-ple, you showed
2. He's the King of kings, the Mas-ter of his peo-ple. He's the

All ... *Cantor*

1. fa-vor, Lord, to those who chose your ways. Still you
2. Lord of lords, the rul-er with-out end. May his

All ... *To Refrain*

1. guard us, Lord, and of-fer us your grace. Ho-ly, ho-ly!
2. fa-vor be up-on us till the end. Ho-ly, ho-ly!

Ed Bolduc
Text and music © 1999, WLP

1. I keep trying to find a life on my own, apart from you.
   I am the king of excuses; I've got one for every selfish thing I do.
   Tell me what's goin' on inside of me?
   I despise my own behavior.
   This only serves to confirm my suspicions
   that I'm still a man in need of a savior.

REFRAIN

I wan-na be in the light___ as you are in__ the light. I wan-na
shine like the stars in the heav - ens.___ O
Lord, be__ my light___ and be my sal - va - tion 'cause
all I want is to__ be in__ the light.
All I want is to__ be in__ the light.

2. The disease of self runs through my blood;
   it's a cancer fatal to my soul.
   Every attempt on my behalf has failed to bring
   this sickness under control.
   Tell me what's goin' on inside of me?
   I despise my own behavior.
   This only serves to confirm my suspicions
   that I'm still a man in need of a savior.

295 In You, Lord

1. Out of my mind, lost in the shadows,
   tired of the doubt eating inside of me—
   Maybe this time, I'll come to my senses
   and find my way out of this insanity.
   But the more I work things out in my own ways,
   the farther I fall away from grace.
   It's so much more than I can comprehend:
   in dying to self, I'll live again.

REFRAIN

In you, Lord. In you, Lord. Take my life and lead __ me in __ the way toward your mer - cy __ and __ truth. __ Your grace is __ in plac - es __ I could nev - er find a - lone; show my heart its right-ful home in you, __ Lord. __

2. Lord of all peace, your word has been spoken,
   sealed in the covenants of history.
   Yet someone like me, so burdened and broken,
   is worthy to share in this great mystery.
   Human nature makes it hard to hear
   that letting go means living without fear.
   Time and again I find it's true:
   in my weakness I find strength in you.

David Yackley
Text and music © 2003, WLP

REFRAIN

In this bread,____ in this wine, we re-ceive your pres-ence di-vine. By your hands____ we are fed, we are raised to new life from the dead: in this bread,____ in this wine.____

1. Here at this table, we come with a hunger,
   we come without reservation.
   Here the weak become strong, the simple find wisdom,
   filled with the joy of salvation.

2. You give us a promise in Body and Blood,
   everlasting covenant:
   All who eat shall not die but live forever,
   freed by bread that is heavensent.

3. From what earth has given and hands have made,
   you have made our divine food.
   Make us holy, O Lord, as you are holy;
   consecrate our lives to you!

Paul L. Berrell
Text and music © 2003, WLP

297 Jesus

1. Lost in a world that has lost trust,
   lost in a world with so, so much,
   I didn't know him! But he's the only way.
   Believe in him! And call out his name: His name is

REFRAIN 1

Je-sus! He's the one! The car-pen-ter's son, the be-got-ten one.

Je - sus! He's the King! The Sav-ior of the world, let the

an-gels sing: Ho-ly, ho-ly, ho-ly, Lord God Al-might-y,

Mak-er of heav - en and earth. Je - sus!

Prince of Peace, de-nied him-self for his love won't cease.

Je - sus! Raise your hands; let the spir-it fill this room, and ev-

- 'ry-bod - y stand. Praise his name for - ev - er, the

bat - tle's won. Je - sus is the vic-tor and death is done!

2. Scared, why are we so scared?
   Do we not know that we're only here for a moment?
   Just one moment. You see, reality is that we're not God.
   We need to build on solid ground,
   open our eyes and see with our minds,
   give in to the fact we're on borrowed time,
   and know that God is by our side,
   even in our difficult, our most difficult times!

REFRAIN 2

Je-sus! Might-y Lord, for-giv-er of all the sins of the world.

Je-sus! Friend of mine, lov-er and teach-er, Son di-vine.

Je-sus is my Sav-ior, I'm not a-fraid to shout to the world

the Mes-si-ah's name. Je-sus! Al-ways near, just

call on his name and know his pres-ence is here. Je-sus!

Broke the bread, gave it to his friends and then he said:

"This is my bod-y given up for you.

Do this in mem-'ry of me."

3. Growin' up in the world today is like matches:
   you get burned if you play.
   All the music and the pictures that you see on the tube
   can mess you up bad, so here's what we do:
   we jam to the beat to put our feet on the floor
   and only sing about the things that bring joy.
   Don't be fooled just because you're young.
   You see, you're smarter than you think, so don't play dumb.
   We all have a good example who will show us the way.
   We all have a good example who taught us how to pray.
   We all have a good example to show us right from wrong.
   We all have a good example. Listen to the words of this song.
   We wanna see grown-ups make a stand
   and do the best that they possibly can,
   work real hard, do the right thing,
   show your children you're not afraid to sing
   about the mystery, the history,
   the story of our life, that includes strife!
   So when we're down and out and need to make a change,
   shout at the top of your voice his holy name! *Refrain 1*

John Angotti
Text and music © 2004, WLP

REFRAIN

Je - sus, hope of the world,____ Je - sus,

light in our dark - ness,____ here we a - wait you, O

Mas - ter Di - vine. Here we re - ceive you in bread and in

wine:____ Je - sus, hope of the world.____

VERSES

1. Come to us, O Son of God! Come to us, O Son of
2. Come to us, O Prom-ised King! Come to us, O Prom-ised
3. Come to us, O Ris - ing Sun! Come to us, O End - less
4. Come to us, O Heart's De - sire! Come to us, O Sav - ing

1.–4. Come, Lord Je - sus!____

1. Man! Come, Son of God! Come, Son of Man!
2. Peace! Come, Prom-ised King! Come, Prom-ised Peace!
3. Light! Come, Ris - ing Sun! Come, End - less Light!
4. Love! Come, Heart's De - sire! Come, Sav - ing Love!

1.–4. Come, Lord Je - sus!____

To Refrain

1. Shep-herd your peo - ple in love!____
2. Come and be Lord of our hearts!____
3. Shat - ter the dark - ness of death!____
4. Ban - ish our doubt and our fear!____

Deanna Light and Paul A. Tate
Text and music © 2001, WLP

299 Just Like You

VERSES

1. Re-vive my heart; re-new my soul. In you O Lord, I
2. Oh, lift me up, God my Fa-ther. In all this world there

1. am made whole. No more in fear will I wan-der
2. is no oth-er. I'm danc-ing in your ho-ly pres-ence,

1. 'cause you're my God, my Lord and lov-er. Like a burn-ing fire,
2. and your glo-ry fills all my sens-es.

1.–2. be my one de-sire. I want to be ho-

REFRAIN

- ly just like you. I want to go where you lead me to.

With reck-less a-ban-don to your truth. I want to fall deep-

1.
- er in love with you.

To Verse 2 | 2. | To Refrain
- er in love with you. I want to be ho-

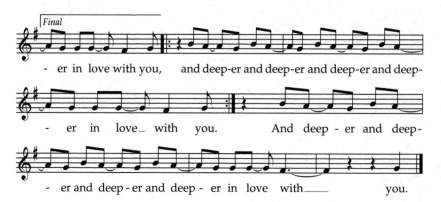

Final

- er in love with you, and deep-er and deep-er and deep-er and deep-

- er in love_ with you. And deep - er and deep-

- er and deep - er and deep - er in love with____ you.

Matt Maher
Text and music © 2001, Matt Maher, pub. by spiritandsong.com®

300 Let Everything That Has Breath

REFRAIN

Let ev-'ry-thing that, ev-'ry-thing that, ev-'ry-thing that
has breath praise the Lord. Let ev-'ry-thing that ev-'ry-thing that,
ev-'ry-thing that has breath praise the Lord.

VERSES

1. Praise you in the morn-ing, praise you in the eve-ning,
2. Praise you in the heav-ens, join - ing with the an - gels,

1. praise you when I'm young and when I'm old.
2. prais - ing you for - ev - er and a day.

1. Praise you when I'm laugh-ing, praise you when I'm griev-ing,
2. Praise you on the earth now, join - ing with cre - a - tion,

1. praise you ev-'ry sea - son of the soul.
2. call - ing all the na - tions to your praise.

If

1.–2. we could see how much you're worth, your pow'r, your might, your

To Refrain

1.–2. end-less love, then sure-ly we would nev - er cease to praise!

Matt Redman
Text and music © 1999, Thankyou Music (KWY)(PRS), admin. by EMI Christian Music Pub.

Let Me Be Your Bethlehem

1. Is there no room in this world for you?
   Oh, let me be your Bethlehem, let me be your Bethlehem.
   It's cold outside; see, I've opened up my door.
   Let my life be your Bethlehem; unto my life may you be born.

2. Is there no place for you to lay your head?
   Oh, let me be your manger, let me be your manger.
   Rest in me and I will rest in you; rest in me, O child, my Savior;
   rest in me, Lord, my Savior.

REFRAIN

Born in a sta-ble with the an-gels close at hand, strength be-came weak-ness that we might un-der-stand, a God who is hun-gry, a king with-out a throne, Em-man-u-el, a child is born. Em-man-u-el, Em-man-u-el, a child is born.

3. Is there no one who will hold you, Lord?
   Oh, let me be your mother, let me be your mother.
   Heaven cannot hold your glory, Lord, yet I hold you in my arms,
   I hold you in my arms!

Danielle Rose
Text and music © 2001, Danielle Rose Skorich, pub. by WLP

302 Let the River Flow

Let the poor man say,— "I am rich in him." Let the

lost man say,— "I am found in him." Oh,

let the riv - er flow. Let the blind man say, "I can

see a-gain." Let the dead man say, "I am born a-gain."

Oh, let the riv - er flow.

Oh, let the riv - er flow.

REFRAIN

Let the riv-er flow. Let the riv-er flow.

Ho - ly Spir-it, come; Move in pow-

- er, let the riv - er_ flow. Let the

riv - er_ flow. Let the riv - er_ flow.

Let the riv - er_ flow.

Darrell Evans
Text and music © 1995, Mercy/Vineyard Pub., admin. by Music Services (ASCAP)

303 Let the Weight of Your Glory Fall

VERSE

Spir - it of __ the Sov-'reign Lord, come and make your pres-

- ence known. Re - veal __ the glo-ry of the Liv - ing God.

Spir-it of __ the Sov-'reign Lord, come and make your pres-

- ence known. Re - veal the glo-ry of the Liv -ing God.

REFRAIN

Let the weight of your glo - ry cov - er __ us. __ Let the life

__ of your riv - er flow. __ Let the truth of your king-dom

reign in __ us. __ Let the weight of __ your glo - ry, _____ let the

1., Final   *To Verse*

weight of __ your glo - ry _____ fall. _____

2. _____ **BRIDGE**

__ We do not seek your hand. We

on - ly seek your __ face. __ We want to know you.

We want to see— you. Re-veal your glo-ry in this place.—

Steve Merkel
Text and music © 1999, Integrity's Hosanna! Music/ASCAP

Lord, Bring Me Home/ 304
Señor, Llévame a Tu Templo/Psalm 84

REFRAIN

— Lord,— bring me home— to your tem - ple.—
Se - ñor,— llé - va - me— a tu tem - plo.—

1. We long to be there and sing out
   our joy,
   to praise you all of our days!
   See how the sparrows fly near
   to you;
   they too sing a song of praise!

2. Happy are those whose strength
   comes from you;
   they fear not the shadows of night!
   Watching and waiting, they long
   for you
   to fill them with love and light!

3. One day with you in your
   holy place
   is better than a lifetime on earth!
   Show us the pathway that leads
   to you;
   prepare us for our rebirth!

4. Hear my prayer, O God!
   Make my home in you!
   Take me, mold me, shape me,
   hold me
   in your everlasting arms!

1. *Yo quiero estar contigo, Señor,*
   cantarte de corazón.
   ¡Como los pájaros cantan unidos
   con toda la creación!

2. *Dichosos los que encuentran*
   en ti
   sus fuerzas, pues no temerán.
   ¡Día tras día, en tu morada
   te alaban sin cesar!

3. *Vale por mil un día en tu*
   templo
   que en cualquier lugar.
   ¡Muéstranos el camino que
   nos lleva a tu santo hogar!

4. *¡Óyeme, O Dios!*
   Quiero estar contigo.
   Yo me entrego enteramente a ti,
   mi amigo fiel.

Sp. tr. by Pedro Rubalcava

Paul A. Tate
Text and music © 1997, WLP

305 Lord, I Believe

REFRAIN

Lord, I believe. Lord, I believe. I believe you are the Christ.

1. Lord, I believe.

2., 3., Final — To Verses
3rd time D.S.

lieve.

VERSE 1

1. I believe you were born of a Virgin, I believe you
1. suffered and died. I believe you rose up
1. from the dead. I believe you are alive.

To Refrain

VERSE 2

2. I believe that you ascended. I believe you
2. poured out your spirit. I believe that you will come a-
2. gain. Maranatha! Come, Lord Jesus.

To Refrain

John Polce
Text and music © 1998, John Polce, ASCAP

VERSE

Lord, I come, take my life. I of-fer it to you a liv-ing sac-ri-fice; By your grace, by your blood I come in-to the Ho-ly of Ho-lies.

REFRAIN

All I want to do is dwell in your pres-ence and drink from the well that nev-er runs dry;

All I want to see is the light of your glo-ry, just one glimpse, just one drink and my soul is sat-is-fied.

Billy Funk
Text and music © 1996, Integrity's Hosanna! Music/ASCAP

307 Lord, Make Us Turn to You/Psalm 80

REFRAIN

Lord,_____ make us turn to you;_____
let us see your face_____ and we shall be_ saved.

1. O shepherd of Israel, hearken,
    from your throne upon the cherubim, shine forth.
   Rouse your power,
    and come to save us.

2. Once again, O LORD of hosts,
    look down from heaven, and see;
   take care of this vine,
    and protect what your right hand has planted,
    the son of man whom you yourself made strong.

3. May your help be with the man of your right hand,
    with the son of man whom you yourself made strong.
   Then we will no more withdraw from you;
    give us new life, and we will call upon your name.

Text (ref.) © 1969, 1981, 1997, ICEL
Text (vss.) © 1998, 1997, 1970, CCD

John Angotti
Music © 2002, WLP

308 Lord, Reign in Me

VERSES

1. O-ver all the earth you reign on high, ev - 'ry moun-tain stream
2. O-ver ev - 'ry thought, o-ver ev - 'ry word may my life re - flect

1. ev - 'ry sun - set_ sky. But my one re - quest,
2. the beau-ty of my_ Lord. 'Cause you mean more to_ me

1. Lord, my on - ly_ aim_ is that you'd reign in me a-gain.
2. than an - y earth-ly_ thing. So won't you reign in me a-gain.

Lord, reign in___ me, reign in your pow'r! O-ver all my dreams, in my dark-est___ hour. You are the Lord of all I___ am, ___ so won't you reign in me a-gain?

Brenton Brown
Text and music © 1998, Vineyard Songs (UK/Eire),
admin. by Music Services o/b/o Vineyard Music Global, Inc. (PRS)

Lord, Send Your Spirit 309

REFRAIN

Lord, send your spir - it___ and re-new the face of the earth.

Lord, send your spir - it___ and re-new the earth.

1. O my soul, bless the Lord in his temple.
   My King, my God, you're great indeed!
   And the creatures bow down and the forests resound
   and the seas rise and fall in your name.

2. You take away our breath and we perish.
   Withhold your love, we turn to clay!
   And the creatures bow down and the forests resound
   and the seas rise and fall in your name.

Text (ref.) © 1969, 1981, 1997, ICEL

Aaron Thompson
Text (vss.) and music © 2005, Aaron Thompson, pub. by WLP

310 Lord, We Are the People/Psalm 24

REFRAIN

Lord, we are the peo-ple who long to see your face.

Lord, we are the peo-ple who long to see_ your face.

1. The earth belongs to the Lord and all that lies within.
   All the people of the world are his.
   It is God who laid the foundations on the seas
   and made it firm upon the flowing waters.

2. Who can climb the mountain, the mountain of the Lord,
   who can stand before his holy throne?
   Only you who remain sinless in your heart
   and never give in to vain or impure desires.

3. You'll receive a blessing, a blessing from the Lord,
   a reward from the God who saves.
   Such it is for the generation seeking God,
   who seek the face of God, the God of Jacob.

Ed Bolduc
Text and music © 2003, WLP

REFRAIN

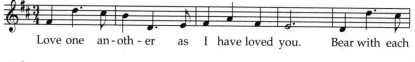

Love one an-oth-er as I have loved you. Bear with each

oth-er and al-ways be true. Live for each oth-er in

u-ni-ty and strength. Give to each oth-er the gift of God's grace.

1. For the Lord is your rock, your fortress, your stronghold.
   It is he who saves you, protects you from death.
   In your lives you shall know how good is the Lord,
   his kindness, his love without end.

2. O give thanks to the Lord, his goodness is endless.
   Give thanks to the Lord for his steadfast love.
   May that love dwell within you, deep in your hearts.
   May his blessings rain down on your days.

3. As the sun in the morning rises in glory,
   as evening draws near, so gently, softly,
   so the love of our Lord is dancing within you,
   shining for all to see.

Feargal King
Text and music © 2000, WLP

312 Make of Our Hands a Throne

REFRAIN

Make of our hands a throne to hold the bread of heav-en,

make of our hearts a home to hold the ver-y wine of

life, in this mys-t'ry, Lord, make us one with you.

VERSES

1. Taste of this good-ness! and feast__ at this ban-quet;
2. You keep your prom-ise, O God__ our__ Sav-ior,
3. From clouds a-bove us you send__ down your bless-ings,
4. With pa-tient yearn-ing, we look to you in hun-ger,
5. This bread now bro-ken, once grain up-on the hill-side,

1. how blest the faith-ful who find shel-ter in God! __
2. hope of the dis-tant isles and all of the earth. You
3. the bread of heav-en and the wa-ters of life! You
4. and through the length of days you feed all your flock. Your
5. is brought to-geth-er and trans-formed in our midst. So

1. Look to your Mak-er, be ra-diant with glo-ry,
2. crown us with good-ness, your fields decked with har-vest.
3. rain down your boun-ty and kiss us with man-na,
4. hands, with a-bun-dance, are wide with your prom-ise,
5. may all your peo-ple be gath-ered to-geth-er,

To Refrain

1. for those who love the Lord are saved from their fears.
2. Your val-leys clothed in wheat re-sound with your joy!
3. bread of the an-gels for our food and our feast.
4. you grant the long-ings of a peo-ple in need!
5. from ev-'ry land in-to the king-dom of love!

Steven C. Warner
Text and music © 2001, WLP

Lord of Life, come and make us your own.
Lord of Love, come let your glory show.
And though we can't see what is meant to be,
be with us, Bread of Life, Lord of all.

REFRAIN

Ho - ly, ho - ly_ Lord,_ ho - ly, ho - ly_ Lord,_ You are the Bread of our life,_ You are the cup of our hope._ Ho - ly, ho - ly_ Lord,_ ho - ly, ho - ly_ Lord,_ Mes - si - ah, Lamb of _ God, our _ Lord. _

Ed Bolduc
Text and music © 1994, WLP

314 My Deliverer

1. Joseph took his wife and her child, and they went to Africa
   to escape the rage of a deadly king.
   There along the banks of the Nile, Jesus listened to the song
   that the captive children used to sing. They were singing,

REFRAIN

My De-liv-er-er is com-ing, my De-liv-er-er is___ stand-ing by.___

Repeat each time

1. He will nev-er break his prom-ise, he has writ-
2. I will nev-er doubt his prom-ise, though I doubt
3. He will nev-er break his prom-ise, though the stars

1. -ten it___ up-on___ the sky.___
2. ___ my heart, I doubt___ my eyes.___
3. ___ should break faith with___ the sky.___

My De-liv-er-er is com-ing, my De-liv-

-er-er is___ stand-ing by.___

2. Through a dry and thirsty land, water from the Kenyan heights
   pours itself out of Lake Sangra's broken heart.
   There in the Sahara winds, Jesus heard the whole world cry
   for the healing that would flow from his own scars.
   The world was singing,

Rich Mullins and Mitch McVicker
Text and music © 1998, White Plastic Bag Music/SESAC, admin. by Music Services

More Love, More Power

1. More love, more pow-er, more of you in my_ life._
2. More faith, more pas-sion, more of you in my_ life._

1. More love, more pow-er, more of you_ in my_ life.
2. More faith, more pas-sion, more of you_ in my_ life.

1. And I will wor-ship you with all of my heart._
2. And I will seek your face with all of my heart._

1. And I will wor-ship you with all of my mind._
2. And I will seek your face with all of my mind._

1. And I will wor-ship you with all of my strength
2. And I will seek your face with all of my strength

1.–2. for you are my God,_____ you are my _ God.

Jude Del Hiero
Text and music © 1987, Mercy/Vineyard Pub.,
admin. by Music Services o/b/o Vineyard Music Global, Inc. (ASCAP)

316 My God Reigns

VERSE

There's no-where else that I'd rath-er__ be__ than

danc-ing__ with you as you sing o - ver me;

There's noth-ing else that I'd rath-er__ do,__ Lord,

1.
__ than to wor-ship you.____

2.
you.____

BRIDGE

So, re-joice, be glad, re-joice, O my soul, for the

Lord, your God, he reigns for-ev-er-more; I__ re - joice,

for my God reigns.____ So, re-joice, be glad, your

Fa-ther and your friend is the Lord, your God, whose rule will nev-er

end; I__ re - joice, for my God reigns.____

REFRAIN

My God reigns_____ and I dance the dance of praise,

_____ my God reigns_____ with a

shout I will pro - claim; "My God reigns,"_____ and I

wor-ship with-out shame,__ my God reigns,_____ and

I will re - joice,__ for my God reigns.

Darrell Patton Evans
Text and music © 1997, Integrity's Hosanna! Music/ASCAP

317 My Soul Is Thirsting/As Morning Breaks/ Psalm 63

REFRAIN

Ref. 1 My soul is thirst-ing for you,_ O Lord, thirst-
Ref. 2 As_ morn-ing breaks I_ look_ to you: be_

1. -ing for you, my God. My soul is thirst-ing for you,
2. _ my_ strength this day._ As_ morn-ing breaks I_ look

1._ O Lord, thirst - ing for you,_ my God.
2._ to you;_ be_ my_ strength this day,_

1._ thirst - ing for you,_ my God._
2._ be_ my_ strength this day._

VERSES 1, 2

1. O_ God, you are_ my God,_ and_
2. Through the day you walk_ with me;_ all the

1. I will al - ways praise_ you. In the shad-ow of_ your wings
2. night your love sur - rounds_ me. To the glo - ry of_ your name

To Refrain

1. _ I cling to_ you_ and you hold me high.
2. _ I lift_ my_ hands, _ I sing your praise.

VERSE 3

I will nev - er be_ a - fraid,_ for I will not be_ a - ban-

3. - doned. E-ven when the road grows long_ and wea-ry your

3. love will res - cue___ me.

Nothing 318

1. Noth-in' can wash___ a - way___ my___ sin.___
2. Noth-in' can make___ the dev - il___ run.___
3. Noth-in' can bring___ me peace with___ God.___
4. Noth-in' can lead___ me to___ your throne.
5. Noth-in' can make___ your peo - ple___ one.___

1. Noth-in' can wash___ a - way___ my___ sin.___
2. Noth-in' can make___ the dev - il___ run.___
3. Noth-in' can bring___ me peace with___ God.___
4. Noth-in' can lead___ me to___ your throne.
5. Noth-in' can make___ your peo - ple___ one.___

1. Noth-in' can wash___ a - way___ my___ sin,___
2. Noth-in' can make___ the dev - il___ run,___
3. Noth-in' can bring___ me peace with___ God,___
4. Noth-in' can lead___ me to___ your throne,
5. Noth-in' can make___ your peo - ple___ one,___

1.–5. noth-in'___ noth-in'___ noth - in' but the blood of Je-

1.–4.
1.–4. - sus.___

5.
5. - sus. Noth-in'___

1.–5. noth-in'___ noth - in' but the blood of Je - sus.

319 No More Fear

VERSES

1. No more fear, though you stum-ble in— the dark -
2. No more fear, though your flesh is bruised and bro -
3. No more fear, though your en - e - mies sur-round—
4. No more fear, though your mind can-not— re - mem -
5. No more fear, though the shad-ows close up-on——
6. No more fear, though they burn a cross be-fore——

1. - ness, no— more fear, though you stum-ble in— the dark-
2. - ken, no— more fear, though your flesh is bruised and bro -
3. —you, no— more fear, though your en - e - mies sur-round
4. - ber, no— more fear, though your mind can-not re - mem -
5. —you, no— more fear, though the shad-ows close up-on——
6. —you, no— more fear, though they burn a cross be-fore——

1. - ness, no— more fear, though you stum-ble in— the dark-
2. - ken, no— more fear, though your flesh is bruised and bro -
3. —you, no— more fear, though your en - e - mies sur-round
4. - ber, no— more fear, though your mind can-not re - mem -
5. —you, no— more fear, though the shad-ows close up-on——
6. —you, no— more fear, though they burn a cross be-fore——

1. - ness,
2. - ken,
3. —you, all you see— be-fore— you lost and fad - ing,
4. - ber,
5. —you,
6. —you,

1.–6. and the lov - ing God who con - quered death is wait-

To Verses

1.–6. - ing for you to call his name.

Final

For you to call his name,

for you to call his name._____

Aaron Thompson
Text and music © 2002, Aaron Thompson, pub. by WLP

O Taste and See 320

REFRAIN

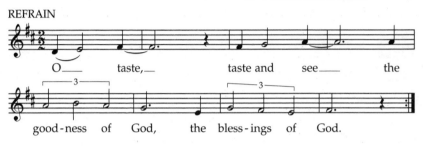

O___ taste,___ taste and see___ the
good-ness of God, the bless-ings of God.

1. I will sing God's praises all the days that I shall live.
   My soul will glory in my God,
   the lowly will hear and be glad.
   O glorify God's name with me,
   together let us rejoice.

2. For God has heard my anguished cries,
   and delivered me from all my foes.
   O look to God that you might shine,
   your faces be radiant with joy.

3. When the poor cry out, God hears and saves them,
   rescues them from their distress.
   God's angel watches near to those
   who look to their God to save them.

4. O taste and see that God is good,
   how happy the ones who find refuge.
   The mighty shall grow weak and hungry,
   those who seek God lack nothing.

5. Come, my children, hear me,
   I will teach you the fear of God.
   Come, all of you who thirst for life
   and seek joy in all of your days.

6. For God is close to the brokenhearted,
   near to those crushed in spirit.
   The hand of God redeems your life,
   a refuge for all those who seek.

Marty Haugen
Text and music © 1993, GIA

321 On Holy Ground

VERSES

1. The heav-ens em - brace the earth, then they sing of the
2. __ Á - bran - se los cie - los, en el nom - bre de
3. Let heav-en and earth sing praise to the one who from

4. Bless earth, wa-ter, fire, and wind. Bless your peo-ple with-
5. La his - to - ria de los Pue - blos se - rá li - bre por
6. U - nit - ed we join the light. We are born of the

1. new birth.__ The earth ech-oes and re -
2. Cris - to__ Dios. Trans - for - men la tie - rra cau-
3. death was_ raised. Let hearts ut - ter words pro -

4. out, with - in. Let beau-ty and birth sur -
5. la ver - dad. La cau-sa es jus - ti - fi -
6. same right.__ We've come to re - lease what's

1. sounds that we are on ho - ly__ ground.
2. ti - va en u - na tie - rra con li - ber - tad.
3. found__ in pro-claim-ing this ho - ly ground.

4. round__ in re - claim-ing this ho - ly__ ground.
5. ca - da. San - ta tie - rra nues-tra se - rá.
6. bound,__ for we are on ho - ly__ ground.

REFRAIN

Cantor Do you be-lieve in free-dom? *All* Yes, we do, Lord! *Cantor* Do you be-lieve in jus - tice?

All Jus-tice for all! ¿Y en la__ nue-va vi - da? *Cantor* ¡En su es - pí - ri - tu!

Cantor ¿Quién es su li-be-ra - ción?__ *All* ¡Tú, Se-ñor! ¡A - rri - ba! ¡Pro-cla - men!

¡San - ta tie - rra! We are on ho - ly ground!

Donna Peña
Text and music © 1992, 1994, GIA

Open My Eyes 322

VERSES

1. O-pen my eyes, Lord.___ Help me to see your
2. O-pen my ears, Lord.___ Help me to hear your
3. O-pen my heart, Lord.___ Help me to love like

1. face. O-pen my eyes, Lord.___ Help me to see. *To Verse 2*
2. voice. O-pen my ears, Lord.___ Help me to hear. *To Bridge*
3. you. O-pen my heart, Lord.___ Help me to love.

BRIDGE

And the first_ shall be last, and our eyes are o-pened, and we'll

hear like nev-er be-fore.___ And we'll speak in new ways, and we'll

To Verse 3

see God's face in plac-es we've nev-er known.

4. I live within you. Deep in your heart, O Love.
   I live within you. Rest now in me.

Jesse Manibusan
Text and music © 1998, Jesse Manibusan, pub. by spiritandsong.com®

323 One Faith

VERSES

1. He__ is the Good Shep-herd and he's
2. And he gave__ to Si - mon Pe - ter and to
3. Yet he'll not__ for - sake his peo-ple; he'll claim his

1. laid down his life for his sheep, so out of man-y na - tions he's
2. all of the twelve the__ keys of the King-dom so
3. sheep for his own. He'll send out his Word to the na - tions, re-

1. gath-ered one fold in one faith.
2. dark-ness shall nev - er pre - vail.
3. gath - er his peo - ple back home.

1. And he has built his church on the
2. But__ some of the shep-herds have pas-tured them-
3. Oh, he is the Good Shep-herd. He's laid down his

1. rock foun-da-tion of faith, on a - pos - tles and proph-ets, who
2. selves on their sheep, so he has come out a - gainst them and
3. life for his sheep. So out of man-y na - tions he's

1. shep-herd the peo-ple in his place.
2. scat-tered his peo - ple of faith.
3. gath-ered one fold in one faith.

REFRAIN

There is one faith, one hope, and one bap-tis-m, one

God and Fa-ther of all, there is one church, one bod-y, one

1.–3.   *To Verses*
Third time to Bridge

life in the Spir-it, now giv-en so free-ly to all.

Final

giv-en so free-ly, giv-en so free-ly to all.

BRIDGE

In good pas-tures, he will shep-herd his peo-ple; on the
He will heal the poor and af-flict-ed, to the

1.   **2.**   *To Refrain*

moun-tain top, he feeds his sheep.
pris-on-er, he brings re- lease.

John Michael Talbot
Text and music © 1988, Birdwing Music (ASCAP), admin. by EMI Christian Music Pub.

324 Open the Eyes of My Heart

VERSE

O-pen the eyes of my heart, Lord; o-pen the eyes of my heart.

— I want to see you, I want to

see you. O-pen the eyes of my heart, Lord;

o-pen the eyes of my heart. I want to see you,

1. To Verse 2., 3.

I want to see you. To see you

REFRAIN

high and lift - ed up,— shin - ing in the light of your glo-

- ry; pour out your pow'r and love, as we sing

1. To Verse 2.

ho - ly, ho - ly, ho - ly. - ly.

FINAL REFRAIN

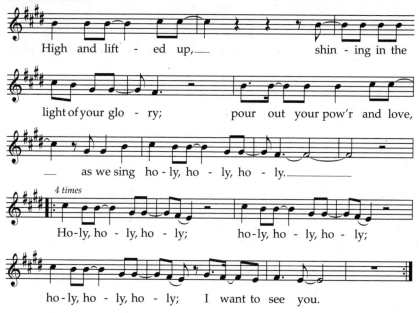

High and lift - ed up,__ shin - ing in the light of your glo - ry; pour out your pow'r and love, __ as we sing ho - ly, ho - ly, ho - ly.____

4 times

Ho-ly, ho - ly, ho - ly; ho-ly, ho - ly, ho - ly; ho - ly, ho - ly, ho - ly; I want to see you.

Paul Baloche
Text and music © 1997, Integrity's Hosanna! Music/ASCAP

325 Once Again

VERSES

1., 2. Je - sus Christ, I think up - on your sac - ri - fice;
3. Now you are_ ex - alt - ed to the high - est_ place,

1., 2. you be - came noth - ing,_ poured out to death.
3. King of the heav - ens, where one day I'll bow._

1., 2. Man - y times I've won-dered at your gift of_ life, and
3. But for now, I mar - vel at this sav - ing grace, and

1.

1., 2. I'm in that place once a - gain.
3. I'm full of praise once a - gain.

2., 3. *To Refrain*

2. I'm in that place_ once a - gain._
3. I'm full of praise once a - gain._

REFRAIN

Once a - gain I look up - on the cross where you died, I'm

hum-bled by your mer-cy and I'm bro-ken in - side. Once a-gain I

Last time *To Verse 3*
Second time to Bridge
2

thank you, once a-gain I pour out my life._

BRIDGE

Thank you for the cross. Thank you for the cross.

To Refrain

Thank you for the cross, my friend.

Matt Redman
Text and music © 1996, Thankyou Music (KWY) (PRS), admin. by EMI Christian Music Pub.

Praise the Lord, My Soul/Psalm 145 326

REFRAIN

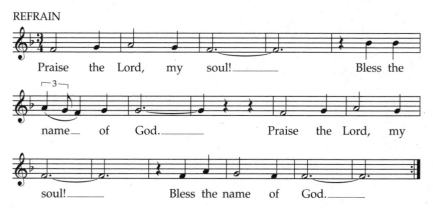

Praise the Lord, my soul! Bless the name of God. Praise the Lord, my soul! Bless the name of God.

1. Oh, the Lord is so faithful forever
   and is just to the oppressed.
   Oh, the Lord gives bread to the hungry
   and sets the captives free.

2. Oh, the Lord heals eyes that are blind
   and raises all who are bowed down.
   Oh, the Lord keeps watch over strangers
   and lifts the helpless child.

Ed Bolduc
Text and music © 2003, WLP

327 Prepare Ye! (John the Rap-tist)

REFRAIN

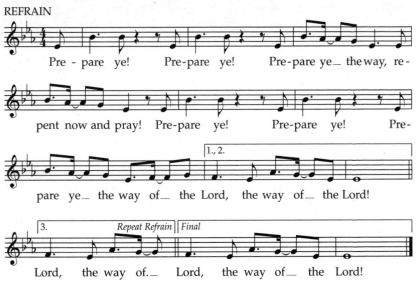

Pre - pare ye! Pre-pare ye! Pre-pare ye— the way, re-
pent now and pray! Pre-pare ye! Pre-pare ye! Prepare ye— the way of— the Lord, the way of— the Lord!
Lord, the way of.— Lord, the way of— the Lord!

1. Prepare the way is the message I'm bringin';
   repentance and faith are the songs that I'm singin'.
   Well, you know the deal: from the desert I came,
   preachin' and teachin' of his holy name.
   I show the way. If you heard that I'm odd,
   just know I'm audacious and I'm workin' for God.
   So don't be dissin' my holy mission
   'cause I can preach with deadly precision.
   I'm takin' my chances, I'm out on a limb,
   escalatin' my rants into shoutin' for him!
   If you say I'm him, well, that I can't handle,
   'cause I can't begin to tie up his sandal.
   If blowin' this joint you're missin' the point,
   'cause the buzz is that Cuz is the one to anoint.
   You'll find out that he's the one,
   blessed Savior, God's own Son.

2. There's no denyin' I'm evangelizin';
   the road to the Lord is through holy baptizin'
   down by the river, if you desire.
   But I'm a pinch-hitter for the one who brings fire.
   When I'm speakin' don't be freakin';
   be seekin' the things you can be tweakin'.
   His word imparts, "Turn back, O man."
   Submerged in your heart you're on track with his plan.
   Don't shoot the messenger. See, I'm a fan
   in the zone just confessin' that he is the man!
   Jesus the man!
   He is the man!
   There's no time to waste so don't you delay.
   Salvation awaits you! It's a brand new day,
   and he'll repay if you obey.
   God is here to stay. Lemme hear ya say:

BRIDGE

David Yackley
Text and music © 2003, WLP

328 Rain Down

REFRAIN

Rain down, rain down, rain down your
love on your peo - ple. Rain down, rain
down, rain down your love, God of life.

VERSES

1. Faith - ful and true is the word of our— God.
2. We who re - vere and find hope in our— God
3. God of cre - a - tion, we long for your truth;

1. All of God's works are so wor - thy of trust.
2. live in the kind - ness and joy of God's wing.
3. you are the wa - ter of life that we thirst.

1. God's mer - cy falls on the just and the— right;
2. God will pro - tect us from dark - ness and— death;
3. Grant that your love, and your peace touch our— hearts,

To Refrain

1. full of God's love is the earth.
2. God will not leave us to starve.
3. all of our hope lies in you.

Jaime Cortez
Text and music © 1992, Jaime Cortez, pub. by OCP

REFRAIN
All

Lift up your heart,_____

Cantor

Lift up your heart,_____ lift up your voice!

lift up your voice! Re-joice, a-gain I say, re-joice!

VERSES

1. Re-joice, the Lord is King!
2. The Lord, our Sav-ior, reigns,
3. Re-joice in glo-rious hope!
4. Cry out to God in praise,

1. Your Lord and King a-dore! Re-
2. The God of truth and love; For
3. For Christ, the Judge, shall come To
4. All you of life and breath. The

To Refrain

1. joice, give thanks and sing, Ex-ult-ant ev-er-more.
2. Christ has purged our sins And reigns en-throned a-bove.
3. take all those who love To their e-ter-nal home.
4. An-cient One of days Has con-quered sin and death.

Ref., vss. 1–3: Charles Wesley, 1707–1788, alt.

Paul A. Tate
Text (vs. 4) and music © 2004, WLP

330 Rise Up in Splendor

REFRAIN

Rise up in splen-dor, rise up in splen-dor, rise up in splen-dor, your light has come.

Rise up in splen-dor, rise up in splen-dor, rise up in splen-dor, your light has come.

VERSES

Rise up in splen-dor, your light has come.

To Refrain

Rise up in splen-dor, your light has come.

1. Rise up in splendor, Jerusalem, your light has come.
   The glory of the LORD will shine upon you.
   See, darkness covers the earth. Thick clouds cover the people.

2. But upon you the LORD God shines
   and over you appears his glory. *Hey!**
   The nations shall walk by your light
   and kings in shining radiance, *yeah.*

3. Raise your eyes and look about you.
   They all gather and they come to you.
   Hey! Your sons come from afar,
   and your daughters in the arms of their nurses.
   And proclaiming the praises of the LORD.

4. Then you shall be radiant at what you see,
   your heart shall throb and overflow.
   For the riches of the sea shall be emptied out before you,
   and the wealth of nations shall be brought to you.
   Caravans of camels shall fill you,
   dromedaries from Midian and Ephah;
   all from Sheba shall come bearing gold, bearing frankincense,
   bearing myrrh, and proclaiming the praises of the LORD.

ALTERNATIVE VERSES FOR GENERAL USE

1. O heaven rejoicing, with every tongue on earth confess
   the lordship of Jesus, the Holy One of Righteousness.

2. O praise to the Father and glory to his only Son.
   Praise to the Spirit, the Holy God, the Three-in-One!

3. God calls us children in Jesus Christ, who sets us free.
   Come, let us worship; let all creation bend the knee!

4. Pray that the Spirit may fall on those who call God's name,
   strength for the weary and healing for the blind and lame.

5. O come to the water, all those who thirst for righteousness.
   Lay down your burdens, put on the robe of holiness!

6. Lord, save your people; from every sin deliver us.
   Send us your mercy; in you alone we place our trust!

7. One is the body, broken on the cross for sin.
   Merciful Savior, transform our hearts from deep within.

8. Look to the heavens and know that Christ will come again.
   Go make disciples and tell them of his love. Amen.

* *Italicized text is not from the Bible.*

Adapted text © 1970, CCD

Aaron Thompson
Alternative text and music © 1999,
Aaron Thompson, pub. by WLP

331 Rise Up, My People

You viper's brood!
Who warned you against the coming retribution?
Then prove your repentance by the fruit which you bear.
I baptize you with water;
but he'll baptize with the Holy Spirit and fire!

REFRAIN

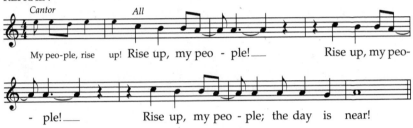

My peo-ple, rise up! Rise up, my peo - ple!__ Rise up, my peo- ple!__ Rise up, my peo - ple; the day is near!

1. Sing out, Jerusalem.
   Rejoice! The day is near!
   Sing out, all you people.
   Wash away your fear, your fear.

2. Prepare ye the way of the Lord.
   Emmanuel shall come to us.

3. Prepare ye the way of the Lord!
   Prepare ye the way of the Lord!
   Prepare ye the way of the Lord!
   Prepare ye the way of the Lord!

FINAL REFRAIN

Rise up, my peo - ple!__

John Angotti
Text and music © 1996, WLP

REFRAIN

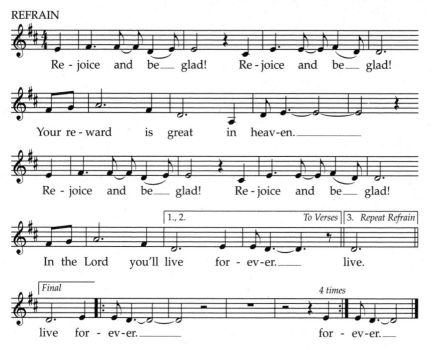

Re - joice and be__ glad! Re - joice and be__ glad!

Your re - ward is great in heav-en._____

Re - joice and be__ glad! Re - joice and be__ glad!

1., 2. / To Verses / 3. Repeat Refrain

In the Lord you'll live for - ev-er.___ live.

Final / 4 times

live for - ev-er._____ for - ev-er.__

1. Blessed are the poor, the poor in spirit,
   for the reign of God is truly theirs.
   Blessed are the ones who live in sorrow;
   consolation will be shared.
   Blessed are the lonely and forgotten;
   they will soon inherit all of the earth.
   Blessed are the ones who long for justice;
   God will satisfy their thirst.

2. Blessed are the ones who show great mercy;
   God will show them mercy in his grace.
   Blessed are the single-hearted people;
   they will live to see his face.
   Blessed are the ones who love and seek peace;
   they are called the children of the Lord.
   Blessed are you when they mock and hurt you,
   for you'll gain heaven's reward.

David Yackley
Text and music © 2003, WLP

333 Salvation Belongs to Our God

VERSES

1. Sal - va - tion be-longs   to our God   who sits up-on   the
2. And we the re-deemed shall be strong   in   pur - pose and

1. throne___   and un - to___ the Lamb,   praise and glo - ry,
2. u - ni-ty,   de-clar-ing a - loud

1.–2. wis-dom and thanks,   hon - or___ and pow-er___ and___ strength

REFRAIN

Be to our God   for-ev - er___ and ev - er,   be   to our God   for-

ev - er___ and ev - er,   be   to our God   for-ev - er___ and ev - er. A-

| **1.** | *To Verse 2* | **2.** | *Repeat Refrain* |

- men!___   - men!___

Final

- men!___   A - men.___

Adrian Howard and Pat Turner
Text and Music © 1985, Restoration Music Ltd./Soverign Music UK

Sacred Heart Song

REFRAIN

Most sa-cred heart of Je - sus tru - ly
pres - ent in the Ho - ly Eu - cha - rist, I place
all my trust in you.

VERSES 1, 2

By the pow - er of___ your pres - ence here work a
In your ten - der___ com - pas - sion, Lord, let your

1. mir - a - cle___ in me,___ drive a - way the dark-
2. dawn of mer - cy shine___ through the hum - ble heart-

To Refrain

1. - ness___ so I can see your glo - ry.
2. - ed.___ Make known your truth and wis - dom.

VERSE 3

3. Late have I loved you. Late have I___ be - lieved in your

To Refrain

3. pow'r to res - cue me___ from pris - ons I have fash - ioned.

Michael John Poirier
Text and music © 1998, Michael John Poirier, pub. by WLP

335 Send Down the Fire

REFRAIN

Send down the fire of your jus - tice,_____

Send down the rains of your love;_____ Come,

send down the Spir - it, breathe life in your peo - ple, and

we shall be peo-ple of God._____

VERSES

1. Call us to be your com - pas - sion,_____
2. Call us to learn of your mer - cy,
3. Call us to an - swer op - pres - sion,_____
4. Call us to wit - ness your King - dom,_____

1. Teach us the song of your love;_____ Give us
2. Teach us the way of your peace;_____ Give us
3. Teach us the fire of your truth;_____ Give us
4. Give us the pres - ence of Christ;_____ May your

1. hearts that sing, Give us deeds that ring, Make us
2. hearts that feel, Give us hands that heal, Make us
3. right - eous souls, 'Til your jus - tice rolls, Make us
4. ho - ly light Keep us shin - ing bright, Ev - er

To Refrain

1. ring with the song of your love._____
2. walk in the way of your peace._____
3. burn with the fire of your truth._____
4. shine with the pres - ence of Christ._____

Marty Haugen
Text and music © 1989, GIA

Send Out Your Spirit, Lord/Psalm 104

REFRAIN

Send out___ your Spir - it, Lord, and re -
new the face of the earth. Send out___ your Spir-
- it, Lord, and re - new the face___ of the earth.

1. Bless the LORD, O my soul!
   LORD, my God, you are great indeed!
   How manifold are your works.
   The earth is full of your creatures.

2. May the glory of the LORD endure forever;
   may the LORD be glad in his works!
   Pleasing to him be my theme;
   I will be glad in the LORD.

3. If you take away their breath, they perish
   and return to their dust.
   When you send forth your spirit, they're created,
   and you renew the face of the earth.

Text (ref.) © 1969, 1981, 1997, ICEL
Text (vss.) © 1998, 1997, 1970, CCD

John Angotti
Music © 2004, WLP

337 Shelter Your Name

REFRAIN

You are all I am not.___ Oh,___ you are all that I am.

___ Break down these walls. Take all my bro-ken-ness.

Re-build me to shel - ter your name._____

Final

build me to shel - ter your name.___

1. Help me forgive myself.
   Help me to lift the cross I've laid upon my soul.
   Help me to look at myself through your eyes,
   to see all that I am, and still be satisfied. Help me forgive myself.

2. Within my secrets, Jesus, there you reside.
   And I need you to reconcile, to renew all that's inside.
   For if I want to love you, then with your love, Jesus,
   I must love myself humbly, too.

Danielle Rose
Text and music © 2001, Danielle Rose Skorich, pub. by WLP

Shine for You

VERSES

1. Touch me, reach in-to my soul. Take me be-yond the world
2. Wake me, o-pen up my eyes. Show me, that I might re-

1. — I know. Move me un-til I learn the dance,
2. -a-lize the truth and turn me un-til I go your way,

1. and teach me to trust you in ev-'ry cir-cum-stance.
2. and give me a pas-sion to live it ev-'ry day.

REFRAIN

So that my life will bless you, so that my light

— will shine for you, so that my life will bless you,

Last time (𝄐)

so that my light will shine for you. Je-sus,

1. *To Verse 2* 2.

— I wan-na shine for you.

BRIDGE

Wash me in the wa-ter, plunge me in-to the flood. Wash me

To Refrain

in the wa-ter, plunge me in-to the flood.

Michael Gleason
Text and music © 2002, Gleasongs (BMI)

339 Shine, Jesus, Shine

VERSES

1. Lord, the light of your love is shin - ing, in the midst of your
2. Lord, I come to your awe - some pres - ence, from the shad-ows in -
3. As we gaze on your king - ly bright-ness, so our fa - ces dis-

1. dark-ness shin-ing. Je-sus, light of the world, shine up - on us.
2. to your ra-diance. By the blood I may en - ter your bright-ness.
3. play your like-ness, ev - er chang-ing from glo - ry to glo - ry.

1. Set us free by the truth you now bring us.
2. Search me, try me, con - sume all my dark - ness.
3. Mir - rored here, may our lives tell your sto - ry.

1.–3. Shine on me. Shine on me.

REFRAIN

Shine, Je - sus, shine; fill this land with the Fa-ther's glo - ry.

Blaze, Spir - it, blaze; set our hearts on fire.

Flow, riv - er, flow; flood the na - tions with grace and mer - cy.

Send forth your word, Lord, and let there be light.

Graham Kendrick
Text and music © 1987, Make Way Music,
admin. by Music Services in the Western Hemisphere

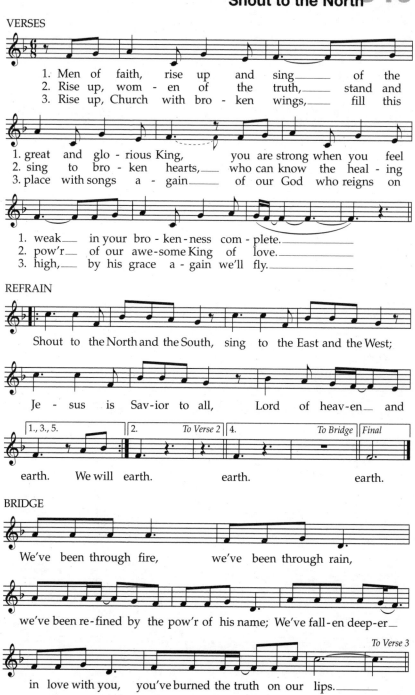

VERSES

1. Men of faith, rise up and sing____ of the
2. Rise up, wom-en of the truth,____ stand and
3. Rise up, Church with bro-ken wings,____ fill this

1. great and glo-rious King, you are strong when you feel
2. sing to bro-ken hearts,____ who can know the heal-ing
3. place with songs a - gain____ of our God who reigns on

1. weak____ in your bro-ken-ness com - plete.____
2. pow'r____ of our awe-some King of love.____
3. high,____ by his grace a - gain we'll fly.____

REFRAIN

Shout to the North and the South, sing to the East and the West;

Je - sus is Sav-ior to all, Lord of heav-en__ and

1., 3., 5. | *2.* *To Verse 2* | *4.* *To Bridge* | *Final*

earth. We will earth. earth. earth.

BRIDGE

We've been through fire, we've been through rain,

we've been re-fined by the pow'r of his name; We've fall-en deep-er__

To Verse 3

in love with you, you've burned the truth on our lips.____

Martin Smith
Text and music © 1995, Curious? Music UK (PRS), admin. by EMI Christian Music Pub.

341 Shout to the Lord

VERSE

My Je-sus, my Sav-ior, Lord, there is none like you;

___ all of my days I want to praise the won-ders of your

might-y love. My com-fort, my shel-ter,

tow-er of ref-uge and strength, let ev-'ry breath, all that I am,

___ nev-er cease to wor - ship you.

REFRAIN

Shout to the Lord, all the earth, let us sing pow-er and maj-es-ty, praise

___ to the King; moun-tains bow down and the seas will roar at the

sound___ of your name.___ I sing for joy___ at the work

___ of your hands; for-ev-er I'll love you, for-ev - er I'll stand.

1. *To Verse*

Noth-ing com-pares to the prom-ise I have in you.

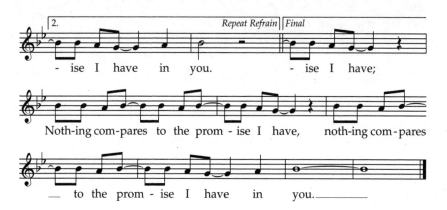

- ise I have in you. - ise I have;

Noth-ing com-pares to the prom - ise I have, noth-ing com-pares

— to the prom - ise I have in you.

Sing Hosanna to Our King 342

REFRAIN

Sing Ho - san - na to our King!_ Sing Ho - san - na to our King!

— Sing Ho - san - na to our King,_ all the earth!_____

To Verses | _Final_

— _____ Sing Ho - san - na!

1. Jesus rides on this day!
   Lift up your hearts in praise to the Son of David, King of Israel!

2. Blessed is he! Blessed is he!
   Blessed is he who comes in the name of the Lord!

3. All glory and praise, all honor to you!
   You are the King of all creation!

4. Praise him with your song! This is where we belong,
   singing praise to our King! Our King!

343 Song of Jubilation

O Lord, I thank you for every blessing given;
I love your awesome way.
You planted in me a whole new way of living;
I'll praise you every day.
O Lord, I thank you for every blessing given;
I love your awesome way.
You planted in me a whole new way of living;
I'll praise you every day.

REFRAIN

I'll sing it out, stand and shout a song of ju - bi - la - tion.
You turned all sor-row in - to joy. Our hearts a - blaze
— in grate-ful praise, ac - claimed by all— cre - a - tion.
Your won-drous love has been re - vealed

1., Final *1st time to Verse*
and in— your mer - cy we— are healed.—

2. *To Refrain*
and in— your mer - cy we— are— healed.—

David Yackley
Text and music © 2003, WLP

1. Are you wonderin' where it is you're goin'?
   Are you wonderin' where you need to be?
   Are you livin' a life with no direction? Can you see? Can you see?
   Hasn't anyone told you what you're missin'?
   Hasn't anyone ever set you free?
   Are you ready to start to make a difference?
   Walk with me, walk with me.

REFRAIN

2. Do you remember the man who walked on water?
   Do you remember he made the blind man see?
   He was livin' a life of love and mercy to show you, to show me.
   Do you remember how he was killed and buried
   and how he walked the road to Calvary?
   How he rose and breathed on us his Spirit,
   saying, "You are free! Live for me!"

BRIDGE

Let your light shine for the world. Let your light shine for the world.
We are here to live a life for God. Let your light shine on us.
Let your light shine for the world. Let your light shine for the world.
We are here to live a life for God. Let your light shine on us.

Ed Bolduc
Text and music © 2002, WLP

345 Spirit of the Living God

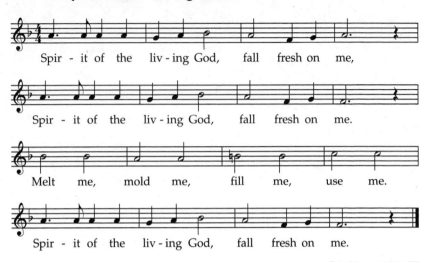

Spir - it of the liv - ing God, fall fresh on me,

Spir - it of the liv - ing God, fall fresh on me.

Melt me, mold me, fill me, use me.

Spir - it of the liv - ing God, fall fresh on me.

Daniel Iverson, 1890–1977
Text and music © 1935, 1963, 1994, Birdwing Music (ASCAP), admin. by EMI Christian Music Pub.

346 Spirit of God

VERSES

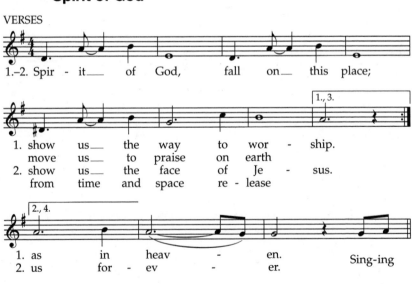

1.–2. Spir - it___ of God, fall on___ this place;

1. show us___ the way to wor - ship.
   move us___ to praise on earth
2. show us___ the face of Je - sus.
   from time and space re - lease

1., 3.

2., 4.

1. as in heav - en.
2. us for - ev - er.

Sing-ing

REFRAIN

with the an - gels, __ cry-ing "Al - le -lu - ia!" __ Sing-ing

with the an - gels, __ cry-ing "Al - le -lu - ia!" __ to the Lamb.

1.   *To Verse 2*

2.
__ to the Lamb.   Sing-ing

FINAL REFRAIN

with the an - gels, __ cry-ing "Al - le - lu - ia!" __

__ Sing-ing with the an - gels, __ cry-ing

1.   **2.**
"Al - le -lu - ia!" __ For-ev-er sing-ing __ to the Lamb,

__ to the Lamb,   to the Lamb.

Michael Gleason
Text and music © 2001, Gleasongs (BMI)

347 Surrender

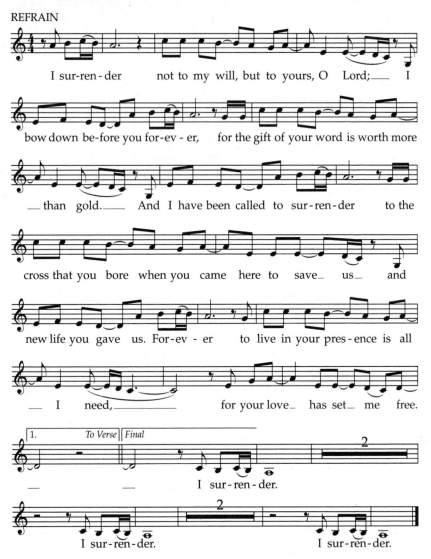

I sur-ren-der   not to my will, but to yours, O Lord;___ I

bow down be-fore you for-ev - er,   for the gift of your word is worth more

___ than gold.___ And I have been called to sur-ren-der   to the

cross that you bore when you came here to save_ us_ and

new life you gave us. For-ev - er   to live in your pres-ence is all

___ I   need,_____   for your love_ has set_ me   free.

1.   To Verse | Final   2

___   ___   I sur-ren-der.

2

I sur-ren-der.   I sur-ren-der.

Lord, I give my heart, give my mind and soul,
everything I have.
All my life I give to you, Lord.
I give my heart, give my mind and soul,
everything I have.
All my life I give to you.
Oh yeah, I was always in control, quite egotistical;
take a virtual miracle to redeem my soul.
My disguise was to maximize the size of the lie that defies.
Only grace would suffice to keep my eyes on the prize.
Then I came to my senses, dropped all pretenses;
hence penitence dispensed with my offenses,
redeemed by your awesome truth,
'cause it's not about me, it's all about you!

David Yackley
Text and music © 2003, WLP

Sweet Child Jesus 348

REFRAIN

Sweet child Je - sus is now sleep-ing, sweet child
Je - sus is now born, is now born.

1. What a dreamer this child shall be!
   From pain and sorrow will the child set us free upon this day!

2. Shall we call him Emmanuel?
   For prophet voices foretold of the wondrous story!

3. Now upon us, an age of peace,
   For joy and gladness come down from on high this holy day!

Joe Mattingly
Text and music © 1995, WLP

349 Take and Eat This Bread

REFRAIN

Take and eat this bread; this is my bod - y.
Take and drink this cup; this is my blood. When you
do this, do this in re - mem-brance of me.

VERSES

1.–4. Come be-fore the ta - ble. Come with all your heart.

1. Come seek - ing heal - ing and for - give - ness.
2. Come seek - ing hope and new di - rec - tion.
3. Come seek - ing com - fort and pro - tec - tion.
4. Come seek - ing clar - i - ty of vi - sion.

To Refrain

1. Come and find love!
2. Come and find faith!
3. Come and find peace!
4. Come and find truth!

Paul A. Tate
Text and music © 2003, WLP

VERSES

1., 4. Ho - li - ness, ho - li - ness
2. Faith - ful - ness, faith - ful - ness } is what I long for.
3. Right-eous-ness, right-eous-ness

1., 4. Ho - li - ness
2. Faith - ful - ness } is what I need.
3. Right-eous - ness

1., 4. Ho - li - ness, ho - li - ness
2. Faith - ful - ness, faith - ful - ness } is what you want from me.
3. Right-eous-ness, right-eous-ness

REFRAIN

Take my heart and form it. Take my mind, trans-

form it. Take my will, con-form

it to yours, to yours, O Lord.

Scott Underwood
Text and music © 1994, Mercy/Vineyard Pub.,
admin. in North America by Music Services o/b/o Vineyard Music Global, Inc. (ASCAP)

351 Teach Me Your Way, O Lord/Psalm 86

REFRAIN

Teach me your way, O__ Lord. Teach me your way, O__ Lord, that I__ may be faith - ful__ in your sight. Teach me your way, O__ Lord.

1. Incline your ear, O Lord; answer me,
     for I'm afflicted and poor.
   Keep my life, for I'm devoted to you;
     save your servant who trusts in you.

2. You are my God; O Lord, have mercy on me,
     for to you I call all the day.
   Gladden the soul of your servant,
     for to you, O Lord, I lift up my soul.

3. For you, O Lord, are good and forgiving,
     abounding in kindness to all who call upon you.
   Hearken, O Lord, to my prayer
     and attend to the sound of my pleading.

Adapted text (ref.) © 1969, 1981, 1997, ICEL
Adapted text (vss.) © 1998, 1997, 1990, CCD

Richard Cheri and Jalonda Robertson
Music © 2004, WLP

Teach Us How to Pray

Lord, teach us how to pray. Teach us what to
say. Teach us how to love, O— my Lord. Teach us how to
pray._____ As we come to wor-ship,
we come to praise your name. For-give us— our
tres-pass-es,— O— my Lord. Teach us how to pray._____

John Angotti
Text and music © 2002, WLP

353 Testify to Love

1. All the colors of the rainbow,
   all the voices of the wind,
   every dream that reaches out,
   that reaches out to find where love begins,
   every word of every story,
   every star in every sky,
   every corner of creation lives to testify.

REFRAIN

For as long as I shall live I will tes-ti-fy to love.

I'll be a wit-ness in the si-lenc-es when words are not e-nough.

With ev-'ry breath I take I will give thanks to God a-bove.

For as long as I shall live I will tes-ti-fy to love.

2. From the mountains to the valleys,
   from the rivers to the sea,
   every hand that reaches out,
   every hand that reaches out to offer peace,
   every simple act of mercy,
   every step to kingdom come,
   all the hope in every heart will speak what love has done.

Paul Field, Henk Pool, Ralph Van Manen, Robert Reikerk
Text and music © 1996, EMI Longitude and Universal-MCA, lic. by Hal Leonard

1. Praise you, Lord, for your goodness.
   Praise you, Lord, for your grace.
   Praise you, Lord, for your mercy in every time and place.
   Trust you, Lord, in the struggle; it's just a matter of faith.
   Help me, Lord, if I stumble.
   In my weakness you will be my strength.

REFRAIN

Lift your voic-es to the sky! Raise your hands and lift_ them high!
— Sing your praise and shout, "Al - might - y!" All you
peo - ple of the land, know that God_ is in_ com-mand.
— Sing your praise and shout, "Al - might - y!"

2. Praise you, Lord, for your goodness.
   Praise you, Lord, for your grace.
   Praise you, Lord, for your mercy in every time and place.
   Trust you, Lord, in the struggle; it's just a matter of faith.
   Help me, Lord, if I stumble.
   In my weakness you will be my strength.

BRIDGE
   Right to give him thanks and praise!
   Right to lift up Jesus' name!
   Right to say, "I do believe he is our Savior."

John Angotti and Ed Bolduc
Text and music © 2004, WLP

REFRAIN

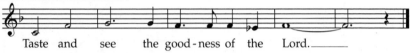

The an-gel of the Lord will res-cue those who fear him.

ALTERNATIVE REFRAIN

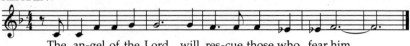

Taste and see the good-ness of the Lord.

1. I will bless the LORD at all times;
    his praise shall be ever in my mouth.
   Let my soul glory in the LORD;
    the lowly will hear me and be glad.

2. Glorify the LORD with me,
    let us together extol his name!
   I sought the LORD, who answered me
    and delivered me from all my fears.

3. Look to him that you may shine with joy!
    Your face may not blush with shame.
   The LORD, who hears the cry of the poor,
    will save your soul from all distress.

4. Everyone who fears the LORD
    will be protected by his holy angel.
   Taste and see the goodness of the LORD.
    How blest are we, his faithful ones!

The Lord Hears the Cry of the Poor/Psalm 34

REFRAIN

The Lord____ hears the cry____ of the poor.

The Lord____ hears the cry____ of the poor.

1. I will bless the LORD at all times;
    his praise shall be in my mouth.
   Let my soul glory in the LORD;
    the lowly will hear and be glad.

2. The LORD confronts the evil ones,
    destroys the remembrance of them.
   The just will cry and the LORD will hear,
    and save them from all their distress.

3. The LORD is close to broken hearts,
    saving those crushed in spirit.
   The LORD redeems his servants' lives,
    all those who take refuge in him.

Text (ref.) © 1969, 1981, 1997, ICEL
Adapted text (vss.) © 1998, 1997, 1970, CCD

Ed Bolduc
Music © 2005, WLP

357 The Lord Is My Light/Psalm 27

REFRAIN

The Lord is my light_ and my_ sal - va - tion._

Whom should I fear? The Lord is my strong-hold and my ref-

- uge.___ How can I be_ a - fraid?

1. There is one thing I ask: to live with you, Lord,
   all of my days and all of my life.

2. And he keeps me secure in times of great fear.
   He shelters my soul, and lifts me high.

3. I believe that I shall see the goodness of my God
   in the land of the living, in the land of the living.

Ed Bolduc
Text and music © 2003, WLP

Hail, Ma-ry, full of grace, the Lord is with you.

Blest are you a-mong wom-en, and blest is the fruit of your

womb, Je - sus, Je - sus.

Blest is the fruit of your womb, Je - sus.

1. Ho-ly Ma-ry, Moth-er of God, pray for us.

Pray for us sin-ners, now and at the hour of our death.

2. Hail, Ma-ry, full of grace. Hail, Ma-ry.

Trad.

James V. Marchionda
Music © 1987, WLP

359 The Way, the Truth, and the Life

He's the Way, the Truth, and the Life.

1. He is the light to the nations,
   shows us the path to salvation.
   He is the true sacrifice.
   He's the Way, the Truth, and the Life.

2. He understands what I'm feeling,
   touches my heart with his healing.
   He's gonna make it all right.
   He's the Way, the Truth, and the Life.

REFRAIN

He is the way that I__ seek. He is the truth __ that I__ speak.__ He is the life_ that I__ need. I don't deserve his mer-cy, yet he died for__ me.__

3. That Easter morning of splendor
   caused Satan's power to surrender.
   Love put an end to our strife.
   He's the Way, the Truth, and the Life.

David Yackley
Text and music © 2003, WLP

The Rock of Faith

1. Do you know where you stand?
   Do you know where your heart is?
   Are you Christ's feet and hands,
   or are you a part of the opposition?
   Open your heart, let Jesus in.
   Open your soul, let the freedom begin.

REFRAIN

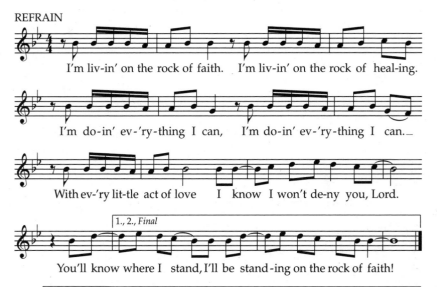

I'm liv-in' on the rock of faith. I'm liv-in' on the rock of heal-ing.

I'm do-in' ev-'ry-thing I can, I'm do-in' ev-'ry-thing I can.

With ev-'ry lit-tle act of love I know I won't de-ny you, Lord.

1., 2., Final

You'll know where I stand, I'll be stand-ing on the rock of faith!

3. *Repeat Refrain*

__ where I stand, you know__ where I stand!

2. To whom shall you go?
   His mercy is calling.
   We face the unknown
   but still we remember that God is in us.
   Open your heart, let peace begin.
   Answer his call, let the healing begin.

BRIDGE
   Faith can move a mountain of doubt.
   Love breaks through and turns your life around.
   You can feel it. When the Spirit is flowing, you reveal it.
   God's love will be showing when you heed his word
   and follow in his ways.

Ed Bolduc
Text and music © 2002, WLP

361 To You, O Lord, I Lift My Soul/Psalm 25

REFRAIN

To you, O Lord, I lift my soul.

1. Lord, make me know your ways; teach me your paths,
   and keep me in the light of your truth,
   for you are my God, my savior.

2. For the Lord is good and righteous,
   revealing the way to those who search for him,
   gently leading the poor and humble.

3. To the ones who seek the Lord, who look to God's word,
   who live in the love of God,
   God will always be near and show them mercy.

Text (ref.) © 1969, 1981, 1997, ICEL

Paul L. Berrell
Text (vss.) and music © 2003, WLP

362 Trading My Sorrows

REFRAIN

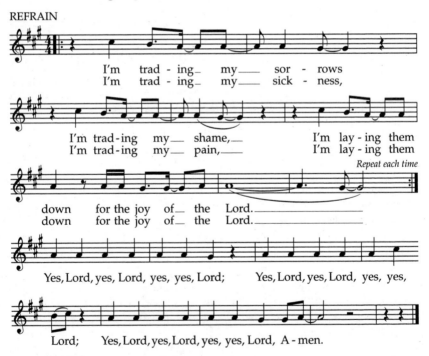

I'm trad-ing my sor-rows
I'm trad-ing my sick-ness,

I'm trad-ing my shame,— I'm lay-ing them
I'm trad-ing my pain,— I'm lay-ing them

Repeat each time

down for the joy of— the Lord.
down for the joy of— the Lord.

Yes, Lord, yes, Lord, yes, yes, Lord; Yes, Lord, yes, Lord, yes, yes,

Lord; Yes, Lord, yes, Lord, yes, yes, Lord, A-men.

VERSES 1, 2

1., 2. I am pressed but not crushed, per-se-cut-ed, not a-ban - doned,

1., 2. struck down but not de - stroyed. I am blessed

1., 2. — be-yond the curse, for his prom-ise will en-dure, that his

1., 2. joy's gon-na be my strength. Though the sor - row may

To Refrain

1., 2. last for the night, his joy— comes with the morn-ing.

VERSE 3

3. Lai lai, lai, lai, lai, lai, lai, lai, lai, lai, lai, lai,

lai, lai, lai, lai, lai, lai, lai, lai, lai, lai, Lai, lai, lai, lai,

1. 2. *To Refrain*

lai, lai, lai, lai, lai, lai, lai, lai, lai.—

Darrell Evans
Text and music © 1998, Integrity's Hosanna! Music/ASCAP

363 This Is the Day/Psalm 118

1. Give thanks to the Lord for he is good.
   His love endures forever.
   Let the house of Israel say:
   "His love endures forever."

2. The Lord's right hand won victory.
   His right hand raised me.
   I shall not die but live
   and recount his wondrous deeds.

3. The stone that the builders rejected
   is now the cornerstone.
   This is the Lord's own deed;
   how marvelous to our eyes.

Ed Bolduc
Text and music © 2003, WLP

364 There Is a Redeemer

VERSES

1. There is a Re-deem-er, Je-sus, God's own Son;___
2. Je-sus, my Re-deem-er, name a-bove all names;__
3. When I stand in glo-ry, I will see his face;___

1. Pre-cious Lamb of God, Mes-si-ah, Ho - ly One.
2. Pre-cious Lamb of God, Mes-si-ah, Hope for_ sin - ners slain.
3. There I'll serve my King for-ev-er in_ that ho - ly place.

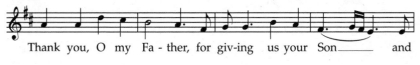

Thank you, O my Fa - ther, for giv-ing us your Son_____ and

leav - ing your Spir - it till the work on_ earth is done.

Melody Green-Sievright
Text and music © 1982, Birdwing Music, BMG Songs, Inc. and Ears to Hear Music (ASCAP),
all admin. by EMI Christian Music Pub. and BMG Music Pub.

Unless a Grain of Wheat 365

REFRAIN

Un - less a grain of wheat shall fall up - on the ground and die,

_____ it shall re-main but a sin-gle grain and not give life._ But

if it dies, if it dies it shall bear fruit to the world.

1. Some days I struggle with my life.
   I turn to you, Lord; hear my cry.
   I fall on my knees.
   O Lord, hear my plea.
   My cross is ever before me.

2. "Father, O my Father, let this cup pass me by,
   for I don't want to taste its poison.
   I don't want to die.
   My cross is heavy, my burdens are many.
   By suffering I will free the world!"

3. Lord, help me through this hour.
   Give to me your power
   so that I may rise again and glorify,
   glorify, glorify your name.

CODA
   Take up the cross in your life and follow Christ,
   then die and rise with him. Take up your cross.

John Angotti
Text and music © 2004, WLP

366 Victory Chant

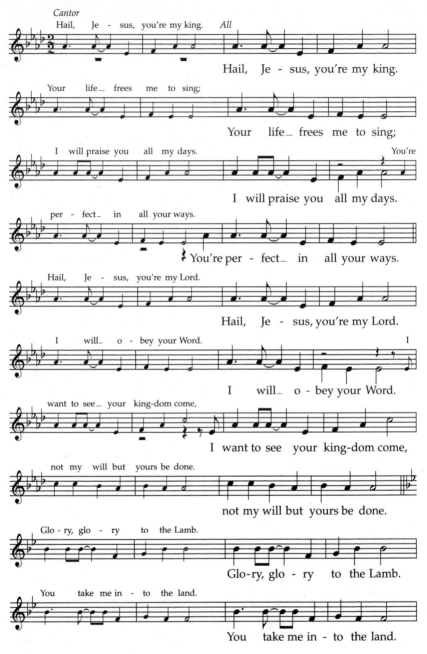

Cantor

Hail, Je - sus, you're my king. *All*

Hail, Je - sus, you're my king.

Your life— frees me to sing;

Your life— frees me to sing;

I will praise you all my days.

You're

I will praise you all my days.

per - fect— in all your ways.

You're per - fect— in all your ways.

Hail, Je - sus, you're my Lord.

Hail, Je - sus, you're my Lord.

I will— o - bey your Word.

I

I will— o - bey your Word.

want to see— your king-dom come,

I want to see your king-dom come,

not my will but yours be done.

not my will but yours be done.

Glo - ry, glo - ry to the Lamb.

Glo-ry, glo - ry to the Lamb.

You take me in - to the land.

You take me in - to the land.

Joseph Vogels
Text and music © 1985, Scripture in Songs (c/o Integrity Music)/ASCAP

367 We Are a Chosen People

REFRAIN

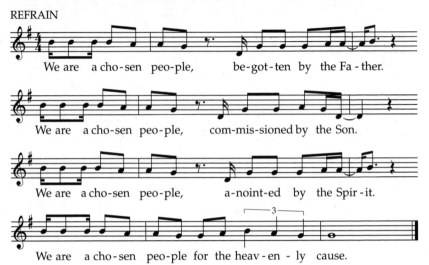

We are a cho-sen peo-ple, be-got-ten by the Fa-ther.

We are a cho-sen peo-ple, com-mis-sioned by the Son.

We are a cho-sen peo-ple, a-noint-ed by the Spir-it.

We are a cho-sen peo-ple for the heav-en-ly cause.

1. Father Almighty, sustainer of life,
   you fashioned creation's birth,
   and in your own image you created us
   to bring your love to the ends of the earth.

2. Go in my name and proclaim the living Gospel.
   Take up your cross and follow me.
   Give food to the hungry; clothe the naked and poor,
   and bring comfort to all those who weep.

3. Send us your Spirit, renew our lives,
   fill us with your living flame.
   Our hearts are glad, our tongues have exulted.
   We go forth in praise of your name!

Paul L. Berrell
Text and music © 2004, WLP

We Belong to God

1. None of us lives as his own
   and none of us dies as his own,
   for while we live we are responsible to God,
   and when we die we die as his servants.

REFRAIN

For both in life and death we be-long to God.

That is why Christ has died for us and will come a - gain.

We shall all ap-pear before the judg-ment seat of God,

for it is writ-ten, "Ev - 'ry knee shall bend be -

fore me and ev - 'ry tongue shall give

praise to God."

2. For we are sure that neither death nor life,
   nor this nor any future ages nor their powers,
   no height, no depth, no creature that thrives
   will come between us and the love of Christ.

3. Give yourselves as sacrifice to God,
   holy and acceptable to the Lord.
   Do not allow your minds to be conformed to this age,
   but let your hearts be ruled by his Spirit.

4. Now not all of us shall fall asleep,
   but all of us are to be changed;
   in the twinkling of an eye, as the last trumpet sounds,
   we shall rise victorious in Christ!

John Flaherty
Text and music © John Flaherty

369 We Believe

REFRAIN

Faith-less and lost once were we,

slaves once but now we are free,

blind once but now we can see, we be-lieve.

1. Moses stood by the burning bush.
   An angel of the Lord came down,
   then Moses knew he was on holy ground.
   Moses stood on Mount Sinai.
   He held the law there in his hands
   and told the people of the Promised Land.
   Just like Moses, we say "Who are we
   to think a burning bush could set us free?"
   Open up our hearts and part our seas.

2. Doubting Thomas, just like us,
   he wasn't in the room that day
   to hear the words that Jesus had to say.
   Doubting Thomas finally saw
   that Jesus was the Risen One,
   the sacrifice that was God's only Son.
   Just like Thomas we all need to see,
   to feel the proof of your divinity,
   to reach for you through all eternity.

3. Savior-seekers on a journey,
   we stumble blindly and we fall,
   and yet we seek the faith to hear your call.
   Savior-seekers far from home,
   we gather in this place to pray,
   a haven for all those who've lost their way.
   Just like Jesus told the Pharisees,
   we must come to face our vanity,
   and not fall prey to our hypocrisy.

BRIDGE

God from God and Light from Light,

We be-lieve.　We be-lieve.

end the darkness of the night.　*We believe. We believe.*
Preacher, teacher, savior, friend,　*We believe. We believe.*
teach us love that never ends.　*We believe. We believe.*
Present here in word and sign,　*We believe. We believe.*
sacrifice in bread and wine,　*We believe. We believe.*
when you will come back again,　*We believe. We believe.*
the dead shall rise and say, "Amen!"

Paul L. Berrell and Paul A. Tate
Text and music © 2001, WLP

370 We Will Be the Light

1. Let your light shine, let us walk in the light.
   Let your love flow, help us to know what is right.
   Let your graces fall to renew us all
   and we will delight as your people, O God!

REFRAIN 1

We will be___ the light. We will be___ the light.

We will be___ the light for all___ to see. We will be___ the love.

We will be___ the love. We will be___ the love so all___ be - lieve.

2. The world cannot see through the darkness it dwells in.
   There's a night to hide the darkness of sin.
   But if we love one another and pardon our brother
   we can let delight back in, light the fire once again!

REFRAIN 2

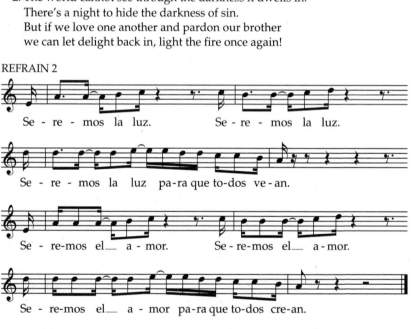

Se - re - mos la luz. Se - re - mos la luz.

Se - re - mos la luz pa-ra que to-dos ve - an.

Se - re-mos el___ a - mor. Se - re-mos el___ a - mor.

Se - re-mos el___ a - mor pa-ra que to-dos cre-an.

A light to all nations, what we need to be.
Look to the testaments, all the experts do agree.
When you live in the darkness you can never be free.
I'm a living example of having sight but couldn't see.
My humanness and stupidness got in the way.
I was busy and dizzy, couldn't tell the night from day.
Blinded by my actions and my personal gain,
didn't know today's pleasure reaped a treasure of pain.
But just like Paul, knocked off my horse,
the Holy Spirit entered, put me back on my course.
I said, "Mirror, mirror, mirror up on the wall,
show me the way before I take a nasty fall."
Then I closed my eyes; before me did I see
the Light of the World. Jesus came to me!
The sacrament and sign's a friend of mine.
I knew that I was walking the borderline.
So now that I'm aware that my ambition is my mission,
to be the light of Christ I've now been commissioned.
A light to all nations is what we need to be.
Look to the testaments; he can set you free! *Refrain 1 followed by Refrain 2*

John Angotti and Noelle Garcia
Text and music © 2004, WLP

371 We Will Serve the Lord

VERSES

1. Wealth can be an i-dol, built of gleam-ing gold,___
2. Pleas-ure is a si-ren, prom-is-ing the flesh,___
3. Pow-er is a hun-ger, burn-ing in the breast, to
4. Fa-ther of all mer-cy, giv-er of all life,___

1. bring-ing dreams of par-a-dise, fu-tures bought and
2. brief re-lief from emp-ti-ness, a hid-ing place from
3. walk a-mong the might-y___ and tram-ple on the
4. here we speak our cov-e-nant a-bove the nois-y

1. sold. Some will choose to gath-er it, all that they can
2. death. Some will choose to chase it___ un-til it leaves them
3. rest. Some will choose to gain it___ by lie or guile or
4. strife. Hear us shout in glo-ry___ a-bove the pa-gan

1. hoard, but
2. bored, but
3. sword, but
4. horde: ___

as for me and my house, we will serve the

1. | To Verse 2 | 2.–4.

1. Lord!

2.–4. Lord!

REFRAIN

As for me and my house, we will serve the Lord,

we will serve the Lord, we will serve the Lord!

Rory Cooney
Text and music © 1985, 2000, spiritandsong.com®

We Will Testify

VERSES

1., 3. God in heav-en, high and ho-ly,
2. Look-ing up-ward, we a-dore you,

1., 3. shown to us by the pow-er of your word,
2. lay-ing down ev-'ry treas-ure at your throne.

1., 3. all the glo-ry giv-en glad-ly
2. None be-side you. None be-fore you.

1., 3. in the praise of your peo-ple who have heard.
2. Ev-er-more you will reign and you a-lone.

1., 3. And with your touch— you turn— our blind-
2. And with your touch— you turn— the dark-

1., 3. -ness in-to sight.—
2. -ness in-to light.—

REFRAIN

We will tes-ti-fy— of your might. We will tes-ti-fy,—

oh,——— we will tes-ti-fy— with our lives, O Lord.

1., 3., Final | *2., 4.* | *Repeat Refrain*

— — O Lord,— O Lord.

Michael Gleason
Text and music © 2001, Gleasongs (BMI)

373 We Fall Down

We fall down, we lay our crowns at the feet___ of Je-

- sus. The great-ness of___ mer-cy and love at the feet

___ of Je - sus. And we cry ho - ly, ho - ly,___ ho-

- ly,___ and we cry ho - ly, ho - ly,___ ho - ly,___ and we cry

ho - ly, ho - ly,___ ho - ly___ is the Lamb._____

Chris Tomlin
Text and music © 1998, Worshiptogether.com Songs (ASCAP), admin. by EMI Christian Music Pub.

374 What a Friend I've Found

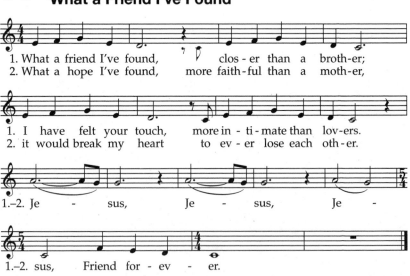

1. What a friend I've found, clos - er than a broth-er;
2. What a hope I've found, more faith-ful than a moth-er,

1. I have felt your touch, more in - ti-mate than lov-ers.
2. it would break my heart to ev - er lose each oth-er.

1.–2. Je - sus, Je - sus, Je-

1.–2. sus, Friend for - ev - er.

Martin Smith
Text and music © 1996, Curious? Music UK (PRS), admin. by EMI Christian Music Pub.

With You by My Side

1. When I'm feeling all alone, and I'm far away from home,
   God, I need you to hear me.
   When my friends all turn away, then I ache to hear you say
   that you are with me through it all.

REFRAIN

You are the light, you're the song that I'm sing - ing;
whom should I fear when you are with___ me? For___
you are my God, and with you___ there is noth-ing I can't

1., 2. | To Verses | 3.

do, with you by my side. side,

(3 times) | 1., 2. | 3.

with you by my side, side.___

2. When I feel all sick inside, with no safe place to hide,
   God, I need you to listen.
   When it seems I can't go on, then I long to hear the song
   reminding me you are my friend.

3. And as I go through my life, I will keep you in my sight
   to walk with me and be my strength.
   God, I know your plan for me: to help all those in need.
   To you alone I give my life.

David Haas
Text and music © 1998, GIA

376 You Alone

VERSE

You____ are the on - ly___ one I____
You___ have___ giv - en me___ more_ than___

need.___ I bow all of me___ at___ your feet.___ I___
I___ could __ ev - er have_ want-ed and I____ want to

wor - ship___ you___ a - lone.
give you my___ heart and my___ soul.

REFRAIN

You____ a - lone___ are Fa-ther and you____ a - lone

___ are___ good; you___ a - lone___ are___ Sav-ior, and you

1.
To Verse 2.

____ a - lone___ are___ God.___ ___ are God.

I'm a - live, I'm a - live,__ I'm a - live, I'm a - live,

1. 2.

I'm a - live, I'm a-live,_ I'm a - live, I'm a - live. ____

FINAL REFRAIN

You___ a - lone___ are Fa-ther and you_____ a - lone

are good; you a-lone are Sav-ior, and you
a-lone are God. are God.

Jack Parker and David Crowder
Text and music © 1998, Worshiptogether.com Songs (ASCAP), admin. by EMI Christian Music Pub.

You Answered Me/Psalm 138 **377**

REFRAIN

Cantor
Lord, on the day I called for help, you an-swered me,

All   *Cantor*   *All*
you an-swered me, you an-swered me. you an-swered me.

Cantor   *All*
Lord, ev-'ry day I call for help,— so

I will give you thanks with all my heart.

1. Kneeling with the angels, I'll sing praise!
   And you shall hear sweet adoration from my mouth.
   And I will worship, oh, I will worship at your holy, holy temple!

2. Because of your great kindness and your truth,
   your name and promise are exalted high above.
   So I will worship, oh, I will worship at your holy, holy temple!

3. Though I walk in darkness and distress,
   you are the shield that will preserve me from my foe.
   I will worship, oh, I will worship at your holy, holy temple!

Text (ref.) © 1969, 1981, 1997, ICEL

Aaron Thompson
Text (vss.) and music © 2005, Aaron Thompson, pub. by WLP

378 You Are Almighty

REFRAIN

Cantor ... *All*

You are al-might-y! You are al-might-y! Al-pha, O - me - ga, the

Cantor ... *All*

first and the last! You are al-might-y! You are al-might-y! Who

is and who was, and who is to come, al-might-y Lord, our God!

VERSES

Cantor

1. To the one who loves us and frees us from sin,
2. To the one who calls us to teach and to serve,
3. To the one who moves us to seek out the truth,

All ... *Cantor*

1.–3. hon-or and glo-ry for-ev-er!
1. Ev-'ry eye shall see him as he
2. Ev-'ry na-tion shall serve him as the
3. Ev-'ry knee shall bow and ev-'ry

To Refrain

1. comes on the clouds and all will wor-ship God's name!
2. rul - er of all; God's king-dom shall not be de - stroyed!
3. tongue con-fess that he a - lone is the Lord!

Paul A. Tate
Text and music © 2001, WLP

You Are My All in All

VERSES

1. You are my strength when I am weak. You are the
2. Tak-ing my sin, my cross, my shame, ris-ing a-

1. treas-ure that I seek. You are my All in All._____
2. gain I bless your name. You are my All in All._____

1. Seek-ing you as a pre-cious jewel, Lord, to give
2. When I fall down you pick me up. When I am

1. up I'd be a fool. You are my All in All.
2. dry you fill my cup. You are my All in All.

REFRAIN

Je - sus, Lamb of God, wor-thy is your name._____

Je - sus, Lamb of God, wor-thy is your name.

Dennis Jernigan

Text and music © 1991, Shepherd's Heart Music, Inc., admin. by Dayspring Music, LLC

380 You Are My Hands

REFRAIN

You are my hands, you are my voice, you are my pres-ence in—

— this world. If you would learn, if you would see,

1., 2.

hum-ble your-self— and fol - low— me.—

3. Repeat Refrain | Final

— low— me.— — low— me.— Oh,—

hum-ble your - self— and fol - low me.—

Hum-ble your - self— and fol - low— me.—

1. Have you let my truth grow cold in your heart?
   Have you forgotten my love?
   Come back to me, come and believe.
   Let me be your joy, let me ease your mind,
   and I will make you strong enough to carry on, to carry on.

2. If you would speak, first you must live
   the love I offer the world.
   Show them my love that they might see;
   let me be your light, let me be your all
   and I will give you love enough to carry on, to carry on.

REFRAIN

You are the light of the world! You are the light of the world! Let your light shine for all to see! You are the light of the world!_____

VERSES

1. Share your bread with the hun-gry;___ shel-ter the lost and the home-less.___ Your wounds shall quick-ly be healed; your light shall break forth like the dawn!_____
2. Hear the cries of the need-y;_____ lis-ten with love and com-pas-sion.___ Our God will an-swer their call and fill them with un-end-ing joy!_____
3. Je-sus tells his dis-ci-ples:___ "You are salt of the earth!_____ Your light must shine be-fore all! Give glo-ry to God's ho-ly name!"_____

To Refrain

Paul A. Tate
Text and music © 1997, WLP

382 You Are My King (Amazing Love)

VERSE

I'm for-giv-en___ be-cause you were for-sak - en.___

I'm ac-cept-ed; you were con-demned.

I'm a-live___ and well, your Spir-it is___with-in___ me___ be-

Repeat Verse

cause___ you died and rose a-gain.___

REFRAIN

A-maz-ing love, how___ can it be___

that you, my King, would die___ for me?___

A-maz-ing love, I___ know it's true;___

and it's my joy to hon - or you in all___ I

To Verse
To Bridge

(⌢) *Last time*

___ do, I hon - or___ you.___

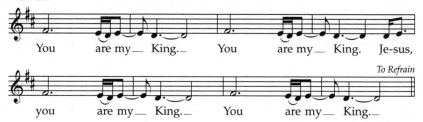

You are my King. You are my King. Je-sus,

To Refrain

you are my King. You are my King.

Billy James Foote
Text and music © 1999, Worshiptogether.com Songs (ASCAP), admin. by EMI Christian Music Pub.

You Are My Rock/Psalm 18 **383**

REFRAIN

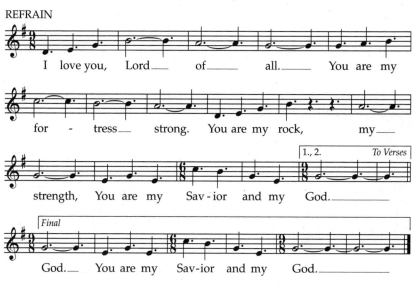

I love you, Lord of all. You are my

for - tress strong. You are my rock, my

1., 2. *To Verses*

strength, You are my Sav-ior and my God.

Final

God. You are my Sav-ior and my God.

1. My God is the rock where I take refuge.
   He is my shield, he is my stronghold, he is my help.
   The Lord is worthy of my praise and the praise of all his people,
   and when I call, I will be saved from all my foes.

2. Long life to the Lord, my Savior.
   Praised be the rock who has saved me from all my foes.
   He has given great triumph to his king.
   And he has shown his great love for his anointed one.

Michael T. Pierce
Text and music © 1998, WLP

384 You Are the Voice

REFRAIN

You____ are the voice____ of the liv - ing God,

call-ing us now to live____ in your love,____ to be

chil-dren of God once a - gain!____

VERSES

Cantor

1. Praise for the light__ that shines through the night, from
2. Praise for the wa - ter that springs from the sea, the
3. Praise for the sing - ing and praise for the dance, with

1. dark - ness to light, from death to new life, and
2. seed that gives life to all who be - lieve, God's
3. new heart and voice,____ all raise the song of

1. praise to the morn - ing that brings forth the sun, to
2. love o - ver - flow - ing, our hearts know the joy, to be
3. praise to cre - a - tion; all heav - en and earth, come

All

1. o - pen our eyes to the Lord!____ To____
2. daugh-ters and sons of the Lord!____ To be
3. sing of the glo - ry of God!____ Come

To Refrain

1. o - pen our eyes to the Lord!____ For
2. daugh-ters and sons of the Lord!____ For
3. sing of the glo - ry of God!____ For

David Haas
Text and music © 1983, 1987, GIA

1. You made me and you know me; you hear me, Lord.
   And every day you show me; you hear me, Lord.
   In the darkness of the night, you will bring me warmth and light,
   for I call to you, my Lord and God.

REFRAIN

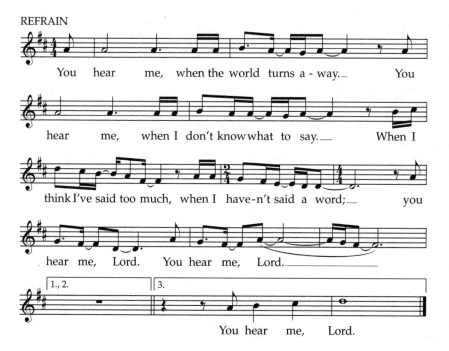

You hear me, when the world turns a-way.__ You
hear me, when I don't know what to say.__ When I
think I've said too much, when I have-n't said a word;__ you
hear me, Lord. You hear me, Lord.__
1., 2. 3.
You hear me, Lord.

2. In times of joy and gladness; you hear me, Lord.
   In times of tears and sadness; you hear me, Lord.
   I may walk this road alone, but I am never on my own.
   You are always there to be my guide.

BRIDGE

Though I may stumble, I may fall, you lift me up; I will stand tall.
You walk beside me all the way, and turn my heart of stone to clay.
So reach me, so teach me, and hide me, and guide me,
protect me, direct me, be near me. And hear me.

Paul L. Berrell and Paul A. Tate
Text and music © 2001, WLP

386 Your Love Is Deep

Your love is_ deep.   Your love is_____ high.   Your love is_

long._____   Your love is_____ wide.   Your love is

Deep-er than my view of grace,   high-er than this world-ly place,

long-er than this road I trav-el,   wid-er than the gap you filled.

1.   Your love is_   D.S.   2. Who shall sep-a-rate_ us?

Who shall sep-a-rate_ us from your love?   Noth-ing can sep-a-rate

_ us.   Noth-ing can_ sep-a-rate us from your love._____

D.S. al Coda   _ Your love is_

✆ CODA   _ wide.   Your love is deep._

Your Love, O Lord

VERSE

Your love, O Lord, reach-es to the heav-ens. Your faith-ful-ness stretch-es to the sky. Your right-eous-ness is like the might-y moun-tains. Yeah. Your jus-tice flows like the o-cean's tide.

REFRAIN

So I will lift my voice to wor-ship you, my King. And I will find my strength in the shad-ow of your wings.

Johnny Mac Powell, Mark D. Lee, Brad Avery, Tai Anderson, and David Carr
Text and music © 2000, New Spring (ASCAP)/Vandura 2500 Songs (ASCAP),
admin. by New Spring (ASCAP)

388 You Know Who I Am

VERSE 1

1. Lord, hear me; I am o-pen. I sur-ren-der all my

1. sin. All my pride gets me no-where, leaves me strand-ed, emp-ty

1. hand-ed___ So shat-ter the dark - ness of___ my life

1. ___ as I car-ry this cross both day and night all the way,

1. ___ all the way,___ to heav - en.___

REFRAIN

You know who I am. Lord, please take my hand and lead me in-

- to com-mu-ni-ty. You know who I am. Lord, help me to stand,

2nd time to Coda

fall-ing in love with your fam-i-ly.___

VERSE 2

2. I con - fess to you, Je-sus, and to

2. you, my broth-ers and sis-ters, that I have sinned and need for-

D.S. al Coda

2. give-ness. Pray for me, and I for you.

CODA

All the way, _ all the way _ to heav - en. _____

All the way, _ all the way _ to heav - en. _____

Matt Maher and Tom Booth
Text and music © 2001, Matt Maher and Tom Booth, pub. by spiritandsong.com®

389 Your Grace Is Enough

VERSES

1. Great is_ your faith - ful-ness, O God_ of Ja - cob;
2. Great is_ your love_and jus - tice, God_ of Ja - cob;

1. you wres-tle with_ the sin-ner's rest - less heart.
2. you use_ the weak to lead the strong.

1. You lead me by___ still wa-ters in - to mer - cy
2. You lead us in___ the song of heav-en's vic - t'ry,

1. where noth - ing can_ keep us_ a - part._____
2. and all_ your peo - ple sing a - long._____ So re -

1.–2. mem - ber your peo - ple,_ re - mem - ber_ your chil - dren, re -

1.–2. mem - ber your prom - ise,_ O God._____ For your

REFRAIN

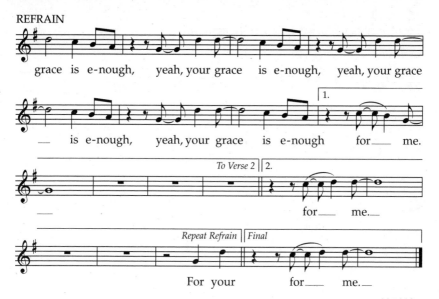

grace is e-nough, yeah, your grace is e-nough, yeah, your grace

_____ is e-nough, yeah, your grace is e-nough for _____ me.

To Verse 2 | 2.

_____ for _____ me. _____

Repeat Refrain | Final

For your for _____ me. _____

Matt Maher
Text and music © 2003, Matt Maher, pub. by spiritandsong.com®

390 Your Love Is Extravagant

REFRAIN

Your love_____ is ex - trav - a - gant._____

_____ Your friend - ship_____

Last time to Coda ⊕

_____ so in - ti - mate._____

I find I'm mov - ing to the rhy - thms of your grace._____

_____ Your fra - grance is in - tox - i - cat - ing in our

se - cret place. Your love_____

_____ is ex - trav - a - gant._____

VERSE

Spread wide— in the arms of Christ—
is the love that cov-ers sin. No great-er love—
have I ev - er known; you con-sid-ered me a friend.
Cap-ture my heart a - gain.

⊕ CODA

3 times

Your love.

Darrell Evans
Text and music © 1998, Integrity's Hosanna! Music/ASCAP

391 Your Love Surpasses Everything I Know

VERSES

1. Dis - il - lu - sioned and de - ject - ed, I___ was filled___
2. Step by step___ I've made this jour - ney through the gloom
3. Now the world's a - live in ways I'd nev - er seen___

1. ___ with doubt, long - ing for a world a - live___ in hope;
2. ___ of night. But I could nev - er face this world a - lone.
3. ___ be - fore;___ bless - ings of your good - ness o - ver-flow.

1. ___ then you took___ my brok - en heart and put a new
2. ___ Though the dark - ness may sur - round me, you are a
3. ___ As I wait___ in joy - ful hope for glo - ry___ that

1. song in my mouth. Now I
2. ra - di-ant light, and I'll sing your prais-es ev - 'ry where I go,
3. ___ is in store, I will

1. To Verse 2

1.–3. ___ 'cause your love sur - pass - es ev - 'ry-thing I___ know.

2. To Refrain | Final

2. ___ 3. ___ Ev - 'ry-thing I know.

REFRAIN

You gave your Son— to take my place, what'd I ev-er

do to de-serve such grace and mer - cy?— Your depth of love

To Verse 3

— tran-scends sim-ply ev - 'ry-thing I can com-pre-hend.

David Yackley
Text and music © 2003, WLP

392 Your Sacrifice

VERSES

1. Lord, we praise you for___ your sac - ri - fice,
2. As we drink this wine and___ eat this bread,
3. There is heal - ing pow'r in the Eu - cha - rist,

1. your ex - am - ple of_____ a per - fect life.
2. we re-mem-ber the thou - sand souls you fed.
3. it makes us one___ in the bod - y of Je - sus Christ.

1. Be - cause of you we can have e - ter - nal life.
2. ___ Bless us, Lord, let our hun - gry souls___ be fed.
3. ___ Lord, we thank you for_____ this gift___ of life.

1. We re - mem - ber your sac - ri - fice.___
2. We re - mem - ber your sac - ri - fice.___
3. We re - mem - ber your sac - ri - fice.___

1. We re - mem - ber your sac - ri - fice.___ *To Verse 2*
2. We re - mem - ber your sac - ri - fice.___ *To Refrain*
3. We re - mem - ber your sac - ri - fice.___ *To Refrain*

REFRAIN

Lord, feed us with your bod-y and blood, and we'll be made whole. U-nite us, ed-i-fy us; we re-mem-ber your sac-ri-fice.

1. To Verse 3

We re-mem-ber your sac-ri-fice.___

2. *Repeat as desired*

___ We give you the glo - ry, the hon-or and praise!

___ We give you the glo - ry, the hon-or and praise!

Thomas Lucas, 1956–2002
Text and music © 2000, WLP

393 You're Worthy of My Praise

VERSES

1. all of my days,   and
2. eyes to your throne,

1. __   and I will fol - low____
2. __   I will trust you,____

1. I will fol - low   all your ways.____
2. I will trust you,   I will trust you a -

1. __   all of your ways._____
2. __   I will trust you a - lone.____

REFRAIN

lone. I will give you all my wor-ship, I will give you

all my praise.____ You a-lone I long to_ wor-ship,

You a-lone are wor-thy of_ my_ praise.

David Ruis

394 Glory to God

REFRAIN

Glo - ry— to God in the high - est, and peace to his peo - ple_____ on earth.

1. Lord God, heavenly King,
   almighty God and Father,
   we worship you, we give you thanks,
   we praise you for your glory.

2. Lord Jesus Christ, only Son of the Father,
   Lord God, Lamb of God,
   you take away the sin of the world:
   have mercy on us;

3. You're seated at the right hand of the Father:
   receive our prayer.
   For you alone are the Holy One,
   you alone are the Lord.

4. You alone are the Most High,
   Jesus Christ the Lord,
   with the Holy Spirit,
   in the glory of God the Father. Amen. Amen.

W. Clifford Petty
Music © 2003, WLP

395 Gospel Acclamation

REFRAIN

Al - le - lu - ia. Al - le - lu - ia. Al - le - lu - ia. Al - le - lu - ia!_____

As the Father has loved me, so I have loved you. Live on in my love.
You will live on in my love if you keep my commandments.

John Towner
Text (vs.) and music © 2004, 2005, WLP

REFRAIN

Al-le, al - le, al - le-lu - ia!__ Al-le, al - le, al - le-lu - ia!__

Al-le, al - le, al - le-lu - ia!__ Al-le-lu - ia!__

1. Speak, O Lord, your servant is listening;
   you have the words of everlasting life.

2. Come, Holy Spirit, fill the hearts of the faithful
   and kindle in them the fire of your love.

3. I am the living bread that came down from heaven;
   whoever eats this bread will live forever.

FINAL REFRAIN

Al-le, al - le, al - le-lu - ia!__ Al-le, al - le, al - le-lu - ia!__

Al-le, al - le, al - le-lu - ia!__ Al-le-lu - ia!__

Al - le-lu - ia!__ Al - le - lu -

ia!__ Al - le - lu - ia!

Text (vss.) © 1969, 1981, 1997, ICEL

John Angotti
Music © 2004, WLP

RESPONSE

Te ro - ga-mos, ó - ye - nos. Lord, hear our prayer.__

Peter M. Kolar
Music © 2001, WLP

398 Mass of Rejoicing—Kyrie

Cantor
Ky - ri - e, e - le - i - son.

All
Ky - ri - e, e - le - i - son.

Chri - ste, e - le - i - son. Ky - ri - e, e - le - i - son.

John Angotti
Music © 2000, WLP

399 Mass of Rejoicing—Glory to God

REFRAIN

Glo - ry— to God in— the high-est,

and peace to— his peo - ple— on earth.

1. Lord God, heavenly King,
   almighty God and Father,
   we worship you, we give you thanks,
   we praise you for your glory.

2. Lord Jesus Christ, only Son of the Father,
   Lord God, Lamb of God,
   you take away the sin of the world:
   have mercy on us; have mercy on us;
   have mercy, have mercy, have mercy on us;
   you are seated at the right hand of the Father:
   receive our prayer.

3. For you alone are the Holy One,
   you alone are the Lord,
   you alone are the Most High,
   Jesus Christ,
   with the Holy Spirit,
   in the glory of God the Father.

Glo - ry___ to God in___ the high-est,

and peace to___ his peo - ple___ on

1. earth. 2. earth.___ A - men.

John Angotti
Music © 2000, WLP

Mass of Rejoicing—Holy, Holy, Holy **400**

REFRAIN

Ho - san - na in___ the high - est.

Repeat first time

Ho - san - na in the high-est.

1. Holy, holy, holy Lord, God of power and might,
   heaven and earth are full of your glory.
   Hosanna in the highest.

2. Blessed is he, blessed is he who comes in the name of the Lord.

John Angotti
Music © 2000, WLP

401 Mass of Rejoicing—Memorial Acclamation A

Christ has died, Christ is ris - en, Christ will come a - gain.

Text © 1973, ICEL

John Angotti
Music © 2000, WLP

402 Mass of Rejoicing—Great Amen

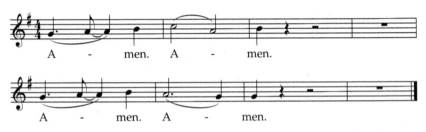

A - men. A - men.

A - men. A - men.

John Angotti
Music © 2000, WLP

403 Mass of Rejoicing—Lamb of God

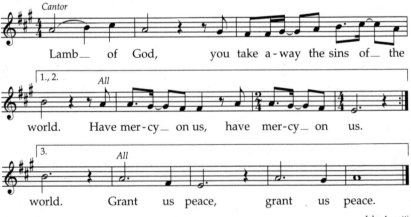

Cantor

Lamb of God, you take a - way the sins of the

1., 2. All

world. Have mer - cy on us, have mer - cy on us.

3. All

world. Grant us peace, grant us peace.

John Angotti
Music © 2000, WLP

Mass of Celebration—Kyrie

Ky - ri - e,   e - le - i - son.   Chri - ste,   e - le - i - son.

Ky - ri - e,   e - le -   i -   son.

Ed Bolduc
Music © 2003, WLP

Mass of Celebration—Glory to God

REFRAIN

Glo - ry to God in the high-est,   and peace to his peo-ple on earth.

1. Lord God, heavenly King,
   almighty God and Father,
   we worship you, we give you thanks,
   we praise you for your glory.

2. Lord Jesus Christ, only Son of the Father,
   Lord God, Lamb of God,
   you take away the sin of the world:
   have mercy on us;
   you are seated at the right hand of the Father:
   receive our prayer.

3. For you alone are the Holy One,
   you alone are the Lord,
   you alone are the Most High,
   Jesus Christ,
   with the Holy Spirit,
   in the glory of God the Father.

FINAL REFRAIN

Glo - ry to God in the high-est,   and peace to his peo-ple on earth.

A -   men, a - men.

Ed Bolduc
Music © 2003, WLP

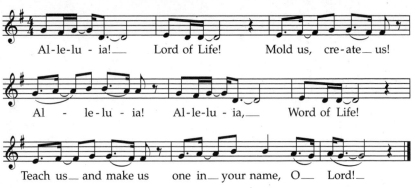

406 Mass of Celebration—Gospel Acclamation

Al-le-lu - ia!__ Lord of Life! Mold us, cre-ate__ us!

Al - le-lu - ia! Al-le-lu - ia,__ Word of Life!

Teach us__ and make us one in__ your name, O__ Lord!__

Ed Bolduc
Text and music © 2003, WLP

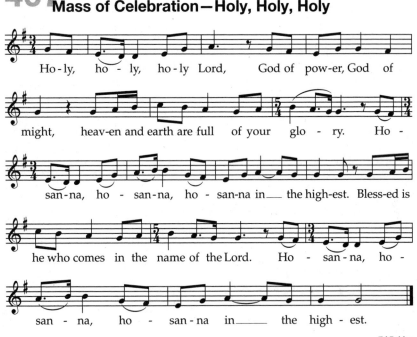

407 Mass of Celebration—Holy, Holy, Holy

Ho - ly, ho - ly, ho - ly Lord, God of pow-er, God of

might, heav-en and earth are full of your glo - ry. Ho -

san-na, ho - san-na, ho - san-na in__ the high-est. Bless-ed is

he who comes in the name of the Lord. Ho - san - na, ho -

san - na, ho - san - na in__ the high - est.

Ed Bolduc
Music © 2003, WLP

Christ has died, Christ is ris - en, Christ will come___ a -

gain.___ Christ will come___ a - gain.

Ed Bolduc
Music © 2005, WLP

Dy-ing you de-stroyed our death, ris-ing you re-stored our

life. Lord Je - sus, come in glo - ry. Lord

Je - sus, come in glo - ry.

Ed Bolduc
Music © 2003, WLP

410 Mass of Celebration— Memorial Acclamation C

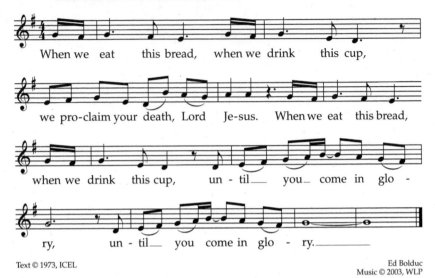

When we eat this bread, when we drink this cup, we pro-claim your death, Lord Je-sus. When we eat this bread, when we drink this cup, un - til you come in glo - ry, un - til you come in glo - ry.

Text © 1973, ICEL

Ed Bolduc
Music © 2003, WLP

411 Mass of Celebration—Great Amen

A - men, a - men, a - men.

Ed Bolduc
Music © 2003, WLP

412 Mass of Celebration—Lamb of God

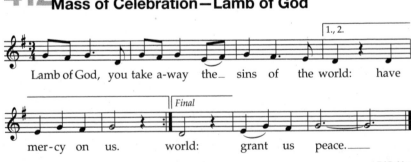

Lamb of God, you take a-way the sins of the world: have mer-cy on us. world: grant us peace.

Ed Bolduc
Music © 2003, WLP

200 Text and music © 2003, World Library Publications.

201 Text and music © 1999, Integrity's Hosanna! Music/ASCAP and LenSongs Publishing/ASCAP, c/o Integrity Media, Inc., 1000 Cody Road, Mobile, AL 36695. All rights reserved. Used by permission.

202 Text and music © 1994, Bobby Fisher. Published by OCP Publications, 5536 NE Hassalo, Portland, OR 97213. All rights reserved. Used with permission.

203 Text and music © 1996, Integrity's Praise! Music/BMI and Praise on the Rock Music/BMI, administered by Integrity's Praise! Music. All rights reserved. Used by permission.

204 Text and music © 1992, New Spring (ASCAP). All rights for the US administered by New Spring (ASCAP). Used by permission.

205 Text of refrain and music © 2003, World Library Publications.

206 Text and music © 2003, World Library Publications.

207 Text and music © 1984, Maranatha Praise, Inc. (administered by The Copyright Company, Nashville, TN). All rights reserved. International copyright secured. Used by permission.

208 Text and music © 1999, World Library Publications.

209 Text and music © 2002, David Kauffman, administered by Music Services (BMI). All rights reserved. Used by permission.

210 Text and music © 1999, Worshiptogether.com, administered by EMI Christian Music Publishing. All rights reserved. Used by permission.

211 Text and music © 2003, Danielle Rose Skorich. Published by World Library Publications.

212 Text and music © 1995, Thankyou Music (KWY) (PRS), administered by EMI Christian Music Publishing. All rights reserved. Used by permission.

213 Text and music © 2000, World Library Publications.

214 Text of the psalm responses from the *Lectionary for Mass*, © 1969, 1981, 1997, International Committee on English in the Liturgy, Inc. All rights reserved. Used by permission. Text of the verses and music © 2005, World Library Publications.

215 Text and music © 2005, Aaron Thompson. Published by World Library Publications.

216 Text and music © 2002, Thankyou Music (KWY) (PRS), administered by EMI Christian Music Publishing. All rights reserved. Used by permission.

217 Text and music © 1995, Mercy/Vineyard Publishing, administered in North America by Music Services o/b/o Vineyard Music Global, Inc. (ASCAP). All rights reserved. Used by permission.

218 Text and music © 2000, World Library Publications.

219 Text and arrangement © 1990, GIA Publications, Inc. All rights reserved. Used by permission.

220 Text and music © 2005, World Library Publications.

221 Text and music © 1993, World Library Publications.

222 Text and music © 2003, World Library Publications.

223 Text and music © 2002, World Library Publications.

224 Text and music © 1999, World Library Publications.

225 Text and music © 1995, World Library Publicationn.

226 Text and music © 2004, World Library Publications.

227 Text and music © 2004, World Library Publications.

228 Text and music © 2004, World Library Publications. All rights reserved. Used by permission.

229 Text and music © 1998, Vineyard Songs (UK/EIRE), administered in North America by Music Services o/b/o Vineyard Music Global, Inc. (PRS).

230 Text and music © 2001, World Library Publications.

231 Text and music © 1994, Maranatha Praise, Inc., administered by The Copyright Company, Nashville, TN. All rights reserved. Used by permission.

232 Text and music © 2002, World Library Publications.

233 Text and music © 2001, World Library Publications.

234 Text and music © 1998, World Library Publications.

235 Text and music © 2002, World Library Publications.

Acknowledgments continued

291 Text of the response from the *Lectionary for Mass*, © 1969, 1981, 1997, International Committee on English in the Liturgy, Inc. All rights reserved. Used by permission. Text of verses and music © 2004, World Library Publications.

292 Text and music © 2003, World Library Publications.

293 Text and music © 1999, World Library Publications.

294 Text and music © 1991, Sparrow Song (BMI), administered by EMI Christian Music Publishing. All rights reserved. Used by permission.

295 Text and music © 2003, World Library Publications.

296 Text and music © 2003, arrangement © 2005, World Library Publications.

297 Text and music © 2004, World Library Publications.

298 Text and music © 2001, World Library Publications.

299 Text and music © 2001, Matt Maher. Published by spiritandsong.com®, 5536 NE Hassalo, Portland, OR 97213. All rights reserved. Used with permission.

300 Text and music © 1999, Thankyou Music (KWY) (PRS), administered by EMI Christian Music Publishing. All rights reserved. Used by permission.

301 Text and music © 2001, Danielle Rose Skorich. Published by World Library Publications.

302 Text and music © 1995, Mercy/Vineyard Publishing, administered in North America by Music Services o/b/o Vineyard Music Global, Inc. (ASCAP). All rights reserved. Used by permission.

303 Text and music © 1999, Integrity's Hosanna! Music/ASCAP. All rights reserved. Used by permission.

304 Text and music © 1997, World Library Publications.

305 Text and music © 1998, John Polce, ASCAP, PO Box 668, Forestdale, RI 02824-0668. jpolcemusic@aol.com.All rights reserved. Used by permission.

306 Text and music © 1996, Integrity's Hosanna! Music/ASCAP. All rights reserved. Used by permission.

307 Text of the psalm response from the *Lectionary for Mass*, © 1969, 1981, 1997, International Committee on English in the Liturgy, Inc. All rights reserved. Used by permission. Text of the verses from the *Lectionary for Mass*, © 1998, 1997, 1970, Confraternity on Christian Doctrine, Inc. All rights reserved. Used by permission. Music © 2002, World Library Publications.

308 Text and music © 1998, Vineyard Songs (UK/EIRE), administered in North America by Music Services o/b/o Vineyard Music Global, Inc. (PRS). All rights reserved. Used by permission.

309 Text of the psalm response from the *Lectionary for Mass*, © 1969, 1981, 1997, International Committee on English in the Liturgy, Inc. All rights reserved. Used by permission. Text of the verses and music © 2005, Aaron Thompson. Published by World Library Publications.

310 Text and music © 2003, World Library Publications.

311 Text and music © 2000, World Library Publications.

312 Text and music © 2001, World Library Publications.

313 Text and music © 1994, World Library Publications.

314 Text and music © 1998, White Plastic Bag Music/SESAC, administered by Music Services. Liturgy Legacy Music/Word/ASCAP. All rights reserved. Used by permission.

315 Text and music © 1987, Mercy/Vineyard Publishing, administered in North America by Music Services o/b/o Vineyard Music Global, Inc. (ASCAP). All rights reserved. Used by permission.

316 Text and music © 1997, Integrity's Hosanna! Music/ASCAP. All rights reserved. Used by permission.

317 Text of Refrain 1 from the *Lectionary for Mass*, © 1969, 1981, 1997, International Committee on English in the Liturgy, Inc. Text of Refrain 2 from the *Liturgy of the Hours*, © 1974, ICEL. All rights reserved. Used by permission. Text of verses and music © 1997, Steve Angrisano. Published by OCP Publications, 5536 NE Hassalo, Portland, OR 97213. All rights reserved. Used with permission.

Acknowledgments continued

351 English translation of the psalm response adapted from the *Lectionary for Mass*, © 1969, 1981, 1997, International Committee on English in the Liturgy, Inc. All rights reserved. Text of the verses adapted from the *Lectionary for Mass*, © 1998, 1997, 1970, Confraternity on Christian Doctrine, Inc. All rights reserved. Used by permission. Music © 2004, World Library Publications.

352 Text and music © 2002, World Library Publications.

353 Text and music © 1996, EMI Longitude and Universal-MCA, licensed by Hal Leonard. All rights reserved. Used by permission.

354 Text and music © 2004, World Library Publications.

355 Text of the psalm response from the *Lectionary for Mass*, © 1969, 1981, 1997, International Committee on English in the Liturgy, Inc. All rights reserved. Used by permission. Text of the verses adapted from the *Lectionary for Mass*, © 1998, 1997, 1970, Confraternity on Christian Doctrine, Inc. All rights reserved. Used by permission. Music © 2004, World Library Publications.

356 Text of the psalm response from the *Lectionary for Mass*, © 1969, 1981, 1997, International Committee on English in the Liturgy, Inc. All rights reserved. Used by permission. Text of the verses adapted from the *Lectionary for Mass*, © 1998, 1997, 1970, Confraternity on Christian Doctrine, Inc. All rights reserved. Used by permission. Music © 2005, World Library Publications.

357 Text and music © 2003, World Library Publications.

358 Music © 1987, World Library Publications.

359 Text and music © 2003, World Library Publications.

360 Text and music © 2002, World Library Publications.

361 Text of the psalm response from the *Lectionary for Mass*, © 1969, 1981, 1997, International Committee on English in the Liturgy, Inc. All rights reserved. Used by permission. Text of the verses and music © 2003, World Library Publications.

362 Text and music © 1998, Integrity's Hosanna! Music/ASCAP. All rights reserved. Used by permission.

363 Text and music © 2003, World Library Publications.

364 Text and music © 1982, Birdwing Music, BMG Songs, Inc., and Ears to Hear Music (ASCAP), all administered by EMI Christian Music Publishing and BMG Music Publishing. All rights reserved. Used by permission.

365 Text and music © 2004, World Library Publications.

366 Text and music © 1985, Scripture in Song (c/o Integrity Music)/ASCAP. All rights reserved. Used by permission.

367 Text and music © 2004, World Library Publications.

368 Text and music © John Flaherty.

369 Text and music © 2001, World Library Publications.

370 Text and music © 2004, World Library Publications.

371 Text and music © 1985, 2000, spiritandsong.com®, 5536 NE Hassalo, Portland, OR 97213. All rights reserved. Used by permission.

372 Text and music © 2001, Gleasongs (BMI). All rights reserved. Used by permission.

373 Text and music © 1998, Worshiptogether.com Songs (ASCAP), administered by EMI Christian Music Publishing. All rights reserved. Used by permission.

374 Text and music © 1996, Curious? Music UK (PRS), administered by EMI Christian Music Publishing. All rights reserved. Used by permission.

375 Text and music © 1998, GIA Publications, Inc. All rights reserved. Used by permission.

376 Text and music © 1998, Worshiptogether.com Songs (ASCAP), administered by EMI Christian Music Publishing. All rights reserved. Used by permission.

377 Text of the psalm response from the *Lectionary for Mass*, © 1969, 1981, 1997, International Committee on English in the Liturgy, Inc. All rights reserved. Used by permission. Text of verses and music © 2005, Aaron Thompson. Published by World Library Publications.

378 Text and music © 2001, World Library Publications.

379 Text and music © 1991, Shepherd's Heart Music, Inc. (administered by Dayspring Music, LLC). All rights reserved. Used by permission

416 Scripture

Scripture continued

Titles and First Lines continued